Patterns and Figures

Algebra

BRITANNICA
Mathematics in Context

TEACHER'S GUIDE

HOLT, RINEHART AND WINSTON

Mathematics in Context is a comprehensive curriculum for the middle grades. It was developed in 1991 through 1997 in collaboration with the Wisconsin Center for Education Research, School of Education, University of Wisconsin-Madison and the Freudenthal Institute at the University of Utrecht, The Netherlands, with the support of the National Science Foundation Grant No. 9054928.

The revision of the curriculum was carried out in 2003 through 2005, with the support of the National Science Foundation Grant No. ESI 0137414.

Opinions expressed are those of the authors and not necessarily those of the Foundation.

Kindt, M.; Roodhardt, A.; Wijers, M.; Dekker, T.; Spence, M. S.; Simon, A. N.; Pligge, M. A.; and Burrill, G. (2006). *Patterns and figures.* In Wisconsin Center for Education Research & Freudenthal Institute (Eds.), *Mathematics in context.* Chicago: Encyclopædia Britannica, Inc.

The Teacher's Guide for this unit was prepared by David C. Webb, Jean Krusi, Sonia Palha, and Truus Dekker.

ISBN 0-03-039842-8

3 4 5 6 073 09 08 07

The *Mathematics in Context* Development Team

Development 1991–1997

The initial version of *Patterns and Figures* was developed by Martin Kindt and
Anton Roodhardt. It was adapted for use in American schools by Mary S. Spence,
Aaron N. Simon, and Margaret A. Pligge.

Wisconsin Center for Education

Research Staff

Thomas A. Romberg
Director

Joan Daniels Pedro
Assistant to the Director

Gail Burrill
Coordinator

Margaret R. Meyer
Coordinator

Project Staff

Jonathan Brendefur
Laura Brinker
James Browne
Jack Burrill
Rose Byrd
Peter Christiansen
Barbara Clarke
Doug Clarke
Beth R. Cole
Fae Dremock
Mary Ann Fix

Sherian Foster
James A, Middleton
Jasmina Milinkovic
Margaret A. Pligge
Mary C. Shafer
Julia A. Shew
Aaron N. Simon
Marvin Smith
Stephanie Z. Smith
Mary S. Spence

Freudenthal Institute Staff

Jan de Lange
Director

Els Feijs
Coordinator

Martin van Reeuwijk
Coordinator

Mieke Abels
Nina Boswinkel
Frans van Galen
Koeno Gravemeijer
Marja van den Heuvel-Panhuizen
Jan Auke de Jong
Vincent Jonker
Ronald Keijzer
Martin Kindt

Jansie Niehaus
Nanda Querelle
Anton Roodhardt
Leen Streefland
Adri Treffers
Monica Wijers
Astrid de Wild

Revision 2003–2005

The revised version of *Patterns and Figures* was developed by Monica Wijers
and Truus Dekker. It was adapted for use in American schools by Gail Burrill.

Wisconsin Center for Education

Research Staff

Thomas A. Romberg
Director

David C. Webb
Coordinator

Gail Burrill
Editorial Coordinator

Margaret A. Pligge
Editorial Coordinator

Project Staff

Sarah Ailts
Beth R. Cole
Erin Hazlett
Teri Hedges
Karen Hoiberg
Carrie Johnson
Jean Krusi
Elaine McGrath

Margaret R. Meyer
Anne Park
Bryna Rappaport
Kathleen A. Steele
Ana C. Stephens
Candace Ulmer
Jill Vettrus

Freudenthal Institute Staff

Jan de Lange
Director

Truus Dekker
Coordinator

Mieke Abels
Content Coordinator

Monica Wijers
Content Coordinator

Arthur Bakker
Peter Boon
Els Feijs
Dédé de Haan
Martin Kindt

Nathalie Kuijpers
Huub Nilwik
Sonia Palha
Nanda Querelle
Martin van Reeuwijk

Cover photo credits: (left to right) © PhotoDisc/Getty Images; © Corbis;
© Getty Images

Illustrations
1, 6 Holly Cooper-Olds; **7** Thomas Spanos/© Encyclopædia Britannica,
Inc.; **8** Christine McCabe/© Encyclopædia Britannica, Inc.; **13** (top)
16 (bottom) Christine McCabe/© Encyclopædia Britannica, Inc.;
25 (top right) Thomas Spanos/© Encyclopædia Britannica, Inc.;
29 Holly Cooper-Olds; **32, 36, 40, 41** Christine McCabe/© Encyclopædia
Britannica, Inc.

Photographs
3 © PhotoDisc/Getty Images; **14** © Corbis; 15 John Foxx/Alamy;
26, 32, 33 © PhotoDisc/Getty Images; **34** SuperStock/Alamy;
43 © PhotoDisc/Getty Images

Contents

Dear Teacher,

Welcome! *Mathematics in Context* is designed to reflect the National Council of Teachers of Mathematics *Principles and Standards for School Mathematics* and the results of decades of classroom-based education research. *Mathematics in Context* was designed according to the principles of Realistic Mathematics Education, a Dutch approach to mathematics teaching and learning. In this approach mathematical content is grounded in a variety of realistic contexts in order to promote student engagement and understanding of mathematics. The term *realistic* is meant to convey that the contexts and mathematics can be made "real in your mind." Rather than relying on you to explain and demonstrate generalized definitions, rules, or algorithms, students investigate questions directly related to a particular context and develop mathematical understanding and meaning from that context.

The curriculum encompasses nine units per grade level. *Patterns and Figures* is designed to be one of the last units in the Algebra strand, but it also lends itself to independent use—to introduce students to number strips, square numbers, number sequences, and triangular and rectangular numbers.

In addition to the Teacher's Guide and Student Books, *Mathematics in Context* offers the following components that will inform and support your teaching:

- *Teacher Implementation Guide,* which provides an overview of the complete system and resources for program implementation;

- *Number Tools* and *Algebra Tools,* which are black-line master resources that serve as intervention sheets or practice pages to support the development of basic skills and extend student understanding of concepts developed in number and algebra units; and

- *Mathematics in Context Online,* which is a rich, balanced resource for teachers, students, and parents looking for additional information, activities, tools, and support to further students' mathematical understanding and achievements.

Thank you for choosing *Mathematics in Context.* We wish you success and inspiration!

Sincerely,

The Mathematics in Context Development Team

Patterns and Figures and the NCTM Principles and Standards for School Mathematics for Grades 6–8

The process standards of Problem Solving, Reasoning and Proof, Communication, Connections, and Representation are addressed across all *Mathematics in Context* units.

In addition, this unit specifically addresses the following PSSM content standards and expectations:

Algebra

In grades 6–8 all students should:

- represent, analyze, and generalize a variety of patterns with tables, graphs, words, and when possible, symbolic rules;
- relate and compare different forms of representation for a relationship;
- develop an initial conceptual understanding of different uses of variables;
- use symbolic algebra to represent situations and to solve problems, especially those that involve linear relationships;
- recognize and generate equivalent forms for simple algebraic expressions; and
- model and solve contextualized problems using various representations, such as graphs, tables, and equations.

Geometry

In grades 6–8 all students should:

- use geometric models to represent and explain numerical and algebraic relationships.

Number and Operations

In grades 6–8 all students should:

- select appropriate methods and tools for computing with decimals from among mental computation, estimation, calculators or computers, and paper and pencil, depending on the situation and apply the selected methods.

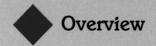
Math in the Unit

Prior Knowledge

This unit assumes that students can do the following:

- add, subtract, multiply, and divide rational numbers;

- understand the order of operations and know how to use parentheses;

- generalize or describe a pattern using words and/or symbols and simple formulas as in *Expressions and Formulas, Comparing Quantities* and *Building Formulas;*

- understand and use simple direct formulas as in *Building Formulas* and *Ups and Downs;*

- recognize relationships among representations: tables, graphs, and formulas;

- understand and use simple recursive formulas; and

- work with whole numbers, including squares.

Math in the Unit

The algebra unit *Patterns and Figures* is part of the Patterns substrand. The Patterns substrand involves looking for and expanding patterns in numbers and tables and building and using expressions and formulas. Student understanding of the structure of algebraic expressions is developed. An important goal for this unit is for students to become flexible in working with expressions and be aware of the relationships between different representations.

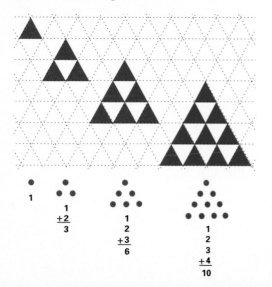

In *Patterns and Figures*, students investigate the use of number strips and dot patterns to represent number sequences. A number sequence with the property that all steps from one number to the next are the same, is called an *arithmetic sequence.*

Such an arithmetic sequence fits with an expression of the form:

$$\text{start number} + \text{step } 3\, n$$

Students also write the recursive and direct formulas that describe them. In a recursive or NEXT-CURRENT formula, the next number or term in a sequence is found by performing an operation on the current term according to a formula. Students learn they can combine sequences by addition and subtraction and find resulting expressions. Number strips form an important tool for this study.

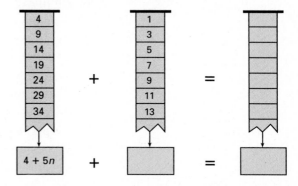

The sequences are added or subtracted by adding or subtracting corresponding numbers; expressions are added or subtracted by adding or subtracting START numbers and steps. Students use Euler's formula and relate this to their work with the vertices, edges, and faces of solids in *Packages and Polygons.*

The area model and number strips are used to introduce square numbers and quadratic expressions.

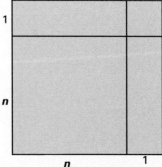

In *Patterns and Figures,* students also encounter or revisit other important mathematical topics such as rectangular and triangular numbers. Tessellations, stacks of cans or pipes, and a ping-pong competition are used for these number patterns. This unit makes connections between algebra and geometry.

Algebra Tools also provides additional practice and extension materials. At the MiC Web site (http://mic.hrw.com), Applets such as Number Strips, Sequences, and Spotting Numbers, can be used to demonstrate concepts and for additional practice. The content of *Patterns and Figures* will be reviewed and expanded in the unit *Algebra Rules!*

When students have finished the unit they will:

- Describe patterns in a sequence of numbers and shapes using words, number strips and formulas to describe them.

  - Students create and use NEXT-CURRENT and direct formulas; formal.

  - Students use an expression to find the connecting sequence.

  - Students more formally understand the concept of equivalent formulas and expressions.

  - Students know that an arithmetic sequence shows constant increase or decrease.

  - Students use odd and even numbers.

  - Students use dot patterns and expressions to describe a sequence of square numbers.

- Make connections between algebra and geometry, using "geometric algebra."

  - Students use dot patterns to describe increase in the sequence of square numbers. They informally explore 1st and 2nd differences.

  - Students use area diagrams and number strips to find equivalent expressions for expressions such as $\left(2\frac{1}{2}\right)^2$; $(n + 1)^2$; $(2n + 1)^2$, and so on.

  - They explore the properties of triangular and rectangular numbers.

  - Students use geometric representations to show that the nth rectangular number can be described by $n(n + 1)$, n starts at 1; and the nth triangular number can be described by $\frac{1}{2}n(n + 1)$, n starts at 1.

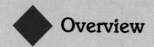

Algebra Strand: An Overview

Mathematical Content

The Algebra strand in *Mathematics in Context* emphasizes algebra as a language used to study relationships among quantities. Students learn to describe these relationships with a variety of representations and to make connections among these representations. The goal is for students to understand the use of algebra as a tool to solve problems that arise in the real world or in the world of mathematics, where symbolic representations can be temporarily freed of meaning to bring a deeper understanding of the problem. Students move from preformal to formal strategies to solve problems, learning to make reasonable choices about which algebraic representation, if any, to use. The goals of the units within the algebra strand are aligned with NCTM's *Principles and Standards for School Mathematics*.

Algebra Tools and Other Resources

The *Algebra Tools* Workbook provides materials for additional practice and further exploration of algebraic concepts that can be used in conjunction with units in the Algebra strand or independently from individual units. The use of a graphing calculator is optional in the student books. The Teacher's Guides provide additional questions if graphing calculators are used.

Organization of the Algebra Strand

The theme of change and relationships encompasses every unit in the Algebra strand. The strand is organized into three substrands: Patterns and Regularities, Restrictions, and Graphing. Note that units within a substrand are also connected to units in other substrands.

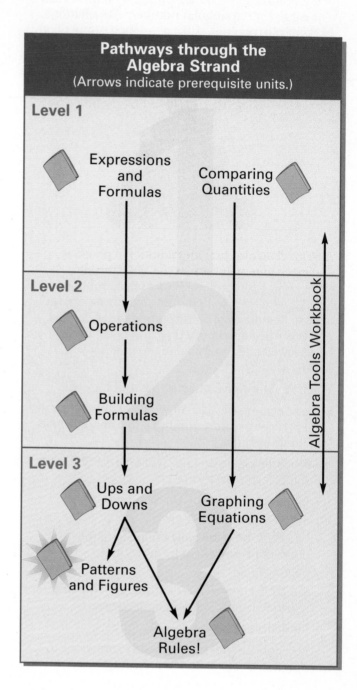

Pathways through the Algebra Strand
(Arrows indicate prerequisite units.)

Level 1
Expressions and Formulas
Comparing Quantities

Level 2
Operations
Building Formulas

Level 3
Ups and Downs
Graphing Equations
Patterns and Figures
Algebra Rules!

Algebra Tools Workbook

Patterns and Regularities

In the Patterns and Regularities substrand, students explore and represent patterns to develop an understanding of formulas, equations, and expressions. The first unit, *Expressions and Formulas*, uses arrow language and arithmetic trees to represent situations. With these tools, students create and use word formulas that are the precursors to algebraic equations. The problem below shows how students use arrow language to write and solve equations with a single unknown.

The students use an arrow string to find the height of a stack of cups.

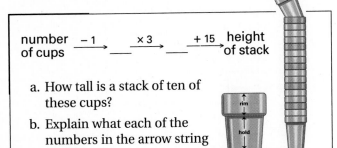

number of cups $\xrightarrow{-1}$ ___ $\xrightarrow{\times 3}$ ___ $\xrightarrow{+15}$ height of stack

a. How tall is a stack of ten of these cups?

b. Explain what each of the numbers in the arrow string represents.

c. These cups need to be stored in a space 50 cm high. How many of these cups can be placed in a stack? Explain how you found your answer.

As problems and calculations become more complicated, students adapt arrow language to include multiplication and division. When dealing with all four arithmetic operations, students learn about the order of operations and use another new tool—arithmetic trees—to help them organize their work and prioritize their calculations. Finally, students begin to generalize their calculations for specific problems using word formulas.

saddle height (in cm) = inseam (in cm) × 1.08
frame height (in cm) = inseam (in cm) × 0.66 + 2

In *Building Formulas*, students explore direct and recursive formulas (formulas in which the current term is used to calculate the next term) to describe patterns. By looking at the repetition of a basic pattern, students are informally introduced to the distributive property. In *Patterns and Figures*, students continue to use and formalize the ideas of direct and recursive formulas and work formally with algebraic expressions, such as $2(n + 1)$.

In a recursive (or NEXT-CURRENT) formula, the next number or term in a sequence is found by performing an operation on the current term according to a formula. For many of the sequences in this unit, the next term is a result of adding or subtracting a fixed number from the current term of the sequence. Operations with linear expressions are connected to "Number Strips," or arithmetic sequences.

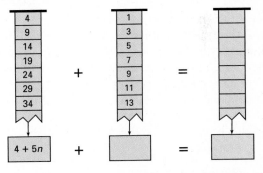

Students learn that they can combine sequences by addition and subtraction. In *Patterns and Figures*, students also encounter or revisit other mathematical topics such as rectangular and triangular numbers. This unit broadens their mathematical experience and makes connections between algebra and geometry.

In the unit *Graphing Equations*, linear equations are solved in an informal and preformal way. The last unit, *Algebra Rules!*, integrates and formalizes the content of algebra substrands. In this unit, a variety of methods to solve linear equations is used in a formal way. Connections to other strands are also formalized. For example, area models of algebraic expressions are used to highlight relationships between symbolic representations and the geometry and measurement strands. In *Algebra Rules!*, students also work with quadratic expressions.

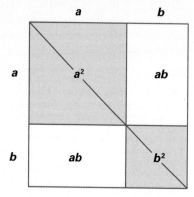

The Patterns and Regularities substrand includes a unit that is closely connected to the Number strand, *Operations*. In this unit, students build on their informal understanding of positive and negative numbers and use these numbers in addition, subtraction, and multiplication. Division of negative numbers is addressed in *Revisiting Numbers* and in *Algebra Rules!*

Restrictions

In the Restrictions substrand, the range of possible solutions to the problems is restricted because the mathematical descriptions of the problem contexts require at least two equations. In *Comparing Quantities*, students explore informal methods for solving systems of equations through nonroutine, yet realistic, problem situations such as running a school store, renting canoes, and ordering in a restaurant.

Within such contexts as bartering, students are introduced to the concept of substitution (exchange) and are encouraged to use symbols to represent problem scenarios. Adding and subtracting relationships graphically and multiplying the values of a graph by a number help students develop a sense of operations with expressions.

To solve problems about the combined costs of varying quantities of such items as pencils and erasers, students use charts to identify possible combinations. They also identify and use the number patterns in these charts to solve problems.

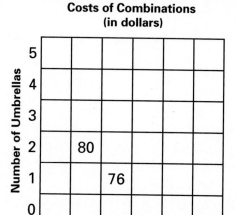

Students' work with problems involving combinations of items is extended as they explore problems about shopping. Given two "picture equations" of different quantities of two items and their combined price, students find the price of a single item. Next, they informally solve problems involving three equations and three variables within the context of a restaurant and the food ordered by people at different tables.

This context also informally introduces matrices. At the end of the unit, students revisit these problem scenarios more formally as they use variables and formal equations to represent and solve problems.

In *Graphing Equations*, students move from locating points using compass directions and bearings to using graphs and algebraic manipulation to find the point of intersection of two lines.

Students may use graphing calculators to support their work as they move from studying slope to using slope to write equations for lines. Visualizing frogs jumping toward or away from a path helps students develop formal algebraic methods for solving a system of linear equations. In *Algebra Rules!*, the relationship between the point of intersection of two lines (A and B) and the *x*-intercept of the difference between those two lines (A – B) is explored. Students also find that parallel lines relate to a system of equations that have no solution.

In *Ups and Downs*, students use equations and graphs to investigate properties of graphs corresponding to a variety of relationships: linear, quadratic, and exponential growth as well as graphs that are periodic.

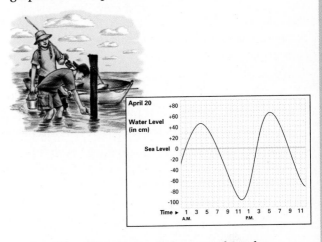

In *Graphing Equations*, students explore the equation of a line in slope and *y*-intercept form. They continuously formalize their knowledge and adopt conventional formal vocabulary and notation, such as origin, quadrant, and *x*-axis, as well as the ordered pairs notation (x, y). In this unit, students use the slope-intercept form of the equation of a line, $y = mx + b$. Students may use graphing calculators to support their work as they move from studying slope to using slope to write equations for lines. Students should now be able to recognize linearity from a graph, a table, and a formula and know the connections between those representations. In the last unit in the Algebra strand, *Algebra Rules!*, these concepts are formalized and the *x*-intercept is introduced. Adding and subtracting relationships graphically and multiplying the values of a graph by a number help students develop a sense of operations with expressions.

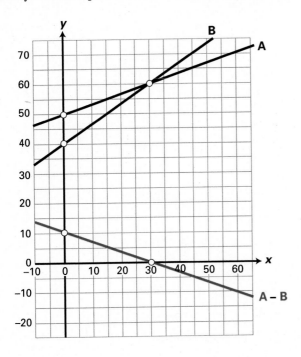

Graphing

The Graphing substrand, which builds on students' experience with graphs in previous number and statistics units, begins with *Expressions and Formulas* where students relate formulas to graphs and read information from a graph.

Operations, which is in the Patterns and Regularities substrand, is also related to the Graphing substrand since it formally introduces the coordinate system.

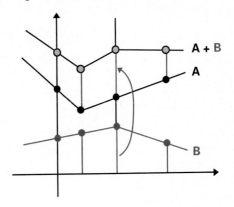

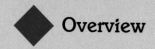

Student Assessment in Mathematics in Context

As recommended by the NCTM *Principles and Standards for School Mathematics* and research on student learning, classroom assessment should be based on evidence drawn from several sources. An assessment plan for a *Mathematics in Context* unit may draw from the following overlapping sources:

- **observation**—As students work individually or in groups, watch for evidence of their understanding of the mathematics.

- **interactive responses**—Listen closely to how students respond to your questions and to the responses of other students.

- **products**—Look for clarity and quality of thought in students' solutions to problems completed in class, homework, extensions, projects, quizzes, and tests.

Assessment Pyramid

When designing a comprehensive assessment program, the assessment tasks used should be distributed across the following three dimensions: mathematics content, levels of reasoning, and difficulty level. The Assessment Pyramid, based on Jan de Lange's theory of assessment, is a model used to suggest how items should be distributed across these three dimensions. Over time, assessment questions should "fill" the pyramid.

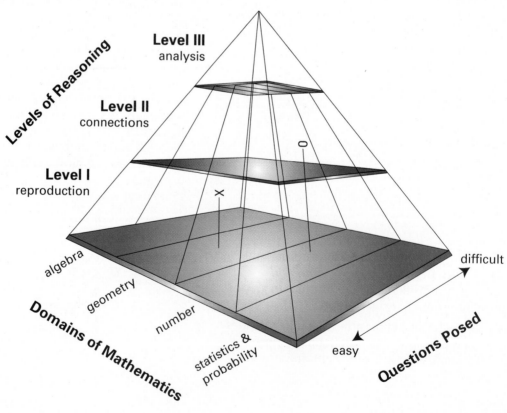

Levels of Reasoning

Level I questions typically address:

- recall of facts and definitions and
- use of technical skills, tools, and standard algorithms.

As shown in the pyramid, Level I questions are not necessarily easy. For example, Level I questions may involve complicated computation problems. In general, Level I questions assess basic knowledge and procedures that may have been emphasized during instruction. The format for this type of question is usually short answer, fill-in, or multiple choice. On a quiz or test, Level I questions closely resemble questions that are regularly found in a given unit substituted with different numbers and/or contexts.

Level II questions require students to:

- integrate information;
- decide which mathematical models or tools to use for a given situation; and
- solve unfamiliar problems in a context, based on the mathematical content of the unit.

Level II questions are typically written to elicit short or extended responses. Students choose their own strategies, use a variety of mathematical models, and explain how they solved a problem.

Level III questions require students to:

- make their own assumptions to solve open-ended problems;
- analyze, interpret, synthesize, reflect; and
- develop one's own strategies or mathematical models.

Level III questions are always open-ended problems. Often, more than one answer is possible and there is a wide variation in reasoning and explanations. There are limitations to the type of Level III problems that students can be reasonably expected to respond to on time-restricted tests.

The instructional decisions a teacher makes as he or she progresses through a unit may influence the level of reasoning required to solve problems. If a method of problem solving required to solve a Level III problem is repeatedly emphasized during instruction, the level of reasoning required to solve a Level II or III problem may be reduced to recall knowledge, or Level I reasoning. A student who does not master a specific algorithm during a unit but solves a problem correctly using his or her own invented strategy may demonstrate higher-level reasoning than a student who memorizes and applies an algorithm.

The "volume" represented by each level of the Assessment Pyramid serves as a guideline for the distribution of problems and use of score points over the three reasoning levels.

These assessment design principles are used throughout *Mathematics in Context*. The Goals and Assessment charts that highlight ongoing assessment opportunities—on pages xvi and xvii of each Teacher's Guide—are organized according to levels of reasoning.

In the Lesson Notes section of the Teacher's Guide, ongoing assessment opportunities are also shown in the Assessment Pyramid icon located at the bottom of the Notes column.

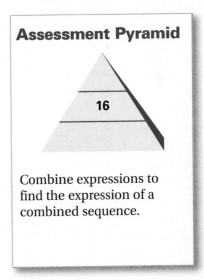

Assessment Pyramid

16

Combine expressions to find the expression of a combined sequence.

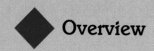

Goals and Assessment

In the *Mathematics in Context* curriculum, unit goals, organized according to levels of reasoning described in the Assessment Pyramid on page xvi, relate to the strand goals and the NCTM *Principles and Standards for School Mathematics*. The *Mathematics in Context* curriculum is designed to help students demonstrate their understanding of mathematics in each of the categories listed below. Ongoing assessment opportunities are also indicated on their respective pages throughout the teacher guide by an Assessment Pyramid icon. It is important to note that the attainment of goals in one category is not a prerequisite to attaining those in another category. In fact, students should progress simultaneously toward several goals in different categories. The Goals and Assessment table is designed to support preparation of an assessment plan.

	Goal	Ongoing Assessment Opportunities	Unit Assessment Opportunities
Level I: Conceptual and Procedural Knowledge	**1.** Use and create dot patterns, number strips, or charts to visualize number sequences.	**Section A** p. 4, #9a **Section D** p. 34, #15a	**Quiz 1** #1, 3a **Test** #2b, 3ab, 4ab
	2. Create and use recursive formulas to describe number sequences.	**Section A** p. 4, #9bc p. 7, #12b **Section B** p. 10, #3b	**Quiz 1** #2b
	3. Create and use expressions and direct formulas to describe number sequences.	**Section A** p. 6, #10d p. 7, #12d **Section B** p. 10, #3c p. 11, #6 p. 16, #19b	**Quiz 1** #1, 2a, 3a **Test** #2cd, 3ab
	4. Understand arithmetic sequences.	**Section B** p. 11, #7a p. 13, #11a	**Quiz 1** #1, 2a, 3a **Quiz 2** #3a, 4a **Test** #2ab
	5. Understand the sequence of square numbers.	**Section C** p. 21, #4 p. 22, #6ab For Further Reflection	**Quiz 2** #1, 2 **Test** #1abc

	Goal	Ongoing Assessment Opportunities	Unit Assessment Opportunities
Level II: **Reasoning,** **Communicating,** **Thinking,** **and Making** **Connections**	**6.** Combine (add or subtract) number sequences and the corresponding expressions.	**Section A** p. 4, #9de **Section B** p. 13, #11bd p. 15, #16 **Section C** p. 25, #17abc	**Quiz 1** #1
	7. Use Euler's formula as an example of combining sequences.	**Section B** p. 16, #19cd	
	8. Justify equivalent expressions.	**Section C** p. 24, #16	**Quiz 1** #3bc **Test** #2d, 3b
	9. Use triangular numbers as examples of describing sequences.	**Section D** p. 29, #4ab, 5ab p. 32, #9 p. 33, #12ab p. 34, #15b	**Test** #4cde

	Goal	Ongoing Assessment Opportunities	Unit Assessment Opportunities
Level III: **Modeling,** **Generalizing,** **and Non-Routine** **Problem Solving**	**10.** Use visual models to represent equivalent expressions and formulas.	**Section A** p. 9, For Further Reflection **Section C** p. 23, #11 p. 25, #17d **Section D** p. 33, #11	**Quiz 2** #3b **Test** #4cd
	11. Generalize a concrete number sequence as an expression.	**Section D** p. 31, #7ab	**Quiz 2** #4b
	12. Use formulas and expressions to describe patterns and sequences in realistic situations.	**Section A** p. 7, #14 **Section B** p. 18, #1ab **Section D** p. 34, #15c p. 35, #20	**Test** #4de

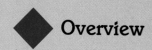

Materials Preparation

The following items are the necessary materials and resources to be used by the teacher and students throughout the unit. For further details, see the Section Overviews and the Materials part of the Hints and Comments section at the top of each teacher page. Note: Some contexts and problems can be enhanced through the use of optional materials. These optional materials are listed in the corresponding Hints and Comments section.

Student Resources

Quantities listed are per student.
- Letter to the Family
- **Student Activity Sheets 1–3**

Teacher Resources

No resources needed

Student Materials

No resources needed

BRITANNICA

Mathematics in Context

Student Material and Teaching Notes

◆ Contents

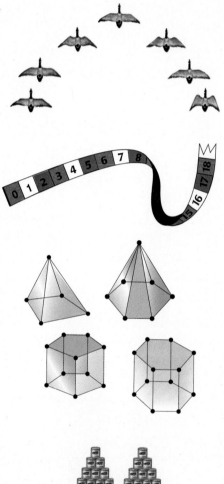

Dear Student,

Welcome to the unit *Patterns and Figures*. In this unit, you will identify patterns in numbers and shapes and describe those patterns using words, diagrams, and formulas.

You have already seen many patterns in mathematics. For patterns with certain characteristics, you will learn rules and formulas to help you describe them. Some of the patterns are described by using geometric figures, and others are described by a mathematical relationship.

Here are two patterns. One is a pattern of dots, and the other is a pattern of geometric shapes.

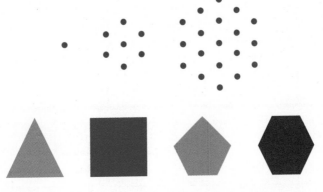

Can you describe the dot pattern? Where do you think the pattern of shapes ends?

As you investigate the *Patterns and Figures* unit, remember that patterns exist in many places—almost anywhere you look! The skills you develop in looking for and describing patterns will always help you, both inside and outside your math classroom.

Sincerely,

The Mathematics in Context Development Team

Section Focus

In this section, students use recursive and direct formulas to represent number sequences and dot patterns. Recursive formulas are used to generate the next term in the number sequence using the current term. Direct formulas, on the other hand, generate any term in the sequence given the pattern number. The term *expression* will be used in later sections to refer to direct formulas without the equal signs.

Note: Students have used recursive and direct formulas in previous algebra units.

Pacing and Planning

Day 1: Number Strips		Student pages 1–4
INTRODUCTION	Problems 1–3	Discuss the patterns on number strips and extend patterns to describe large numbers.
CLASSWORK	Problems 4–8	Investigate the relationship between number strips, dot patterns, recursive formulas, and direct formulas.
HOMEWORK	Problem 9	Create a chart that lists the results of adding combinations of red, white, and blue numbers on a number strip.

Day 2: V- and W-Formations		Student pages 4–7
INTRODUCTION	Review homework.	Review homework from Day 1.
CLASSWORK	Problems 10–12	Write recursive and direct formulas for V and W dot patterns.
HOMEWORK	Problems 13–14	Compare the V and W dot patterns and determine the largest W-pattern that can be made with 200 dots.

Day 3: Summary		Student pages 7–9
INTRODUCTION	Review homework.	Review homework from Day 2.
CLASSWORK	Check Your Work For Further Reflection	Student self-assessment: Write recursive and direct formulas to represent dot patterns.
HOMEWORK	Additional Practice, Section A, page 39	Additional practice creating recursive and direct formulas for various patterns.

Additional Resources: *Algebra Tools*, Additional Practice, Section A, Student Book page 39

Materials

Student Resources

Quantities listed are per student.

- Letter to the Family
- **Student Activity Sheet 1**

Teachers Resources

No resources required

Student Materials

No resources required

* See Hints and Comments for optional materials

Learning Lines

Patterns and Regularities

Students discuss color patterns on number strips and extend the patterns to describe large numbers. For example, on a number strip with three alternating colors, students use the multiples of three to determine the color of a large number on the number strip.

Next, students investigate the use of dot patterns and formulas to represent the color patterns on the number strip. After writing formulas for the even and odd number sequence, students investigate recursive formulas for these patterns and review the terminology for recursive and direct formulas. Next, they investigate W and V dot patterns by analyzing the relationship between the pattern number and the number of dots. They then write recursive and direct formulas for W and V dot patterns.

Models

Students investigate the use of dot patterns to represent number sequences.

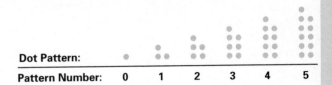

Dot Pattern:						
Pattern Number:	0	1	2	3	4	5

At the End of this Section: Learning Outcomes

Students use and create dot patterns, number strips, or charts to visualize number sequences. They also use and create recursive formulas to describe number sequences

Notes

Make samples of the odd-even and red-white-blue number strips—or have students make them—to post above the blackboard for reference. Printing numbers on card stock makes it easy to store.

The title of the unit is *Patterns and Figures.* Ask students for some examples of patterns in their lives. You may also want to talk about the meaning of the word *figure* in mathematics.

1 You might like to take a few minutes to discuss what the number strip would look like if it extended to the left of zero.

Patterns

Number Strips

Patterns are at the heart of mathematics, and you can find patterns by looking at shapes, numbers, and many other things. In this unit, you will discover and explore patterns and describe them with numbers and formulas.

Below, numbers starting with 0 are shown on a paper strip. The strip has alternating red and white colors.

1. Notice that the right end of the strip looks different from the left end. What do you think that indicates?

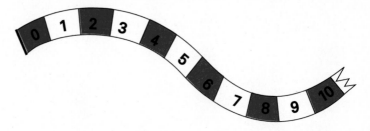

2. **a.** What do the white numbers have in common?

   b. Think of a large number not shown on the strip. How can you tell the color for your number?

Reaching All Learners

Intervention

Be sure students understand that the torn end means that the pattern would continue on. Students can tell you the next numbers and their colors.

Extension

Ask students to create a number pattern on a strip of paper. Use a few examples each day as an opener. Ask the class for the next few terms and the formula if appropriate. Alternatively, this could be an activity for advanced learners.

Solutions and Samples

1. The left end of the strip has a straight edge implying the beginning or starting point. The right side goes on forever. In other words, this is an infinite sequence.

2. **a.** Answers may vary. Some students may respond that the white numbers are odd numbers. Others may say they are always two apart.

   b. The white numbers and red numbers both differ by two each time. If the last digit is even, the number itself is even and the color is red. If the last digit is odd, then the number is odd and the color is white.

Hints and Comments

Overview

Students read about the importance of patterns in mathematics. They study a number strip in which even and odd numbers have different colors, and they find the color of a large number not shown on the strip.

Planning

Have students read the introductory text on page 1 of the Student Book. Students may then work in small groups on problems 1 and 2. Be sure to discuss their answers for both problems.

Comments About the Solutions

2. **a.** Most students will answer that the white numbers are odd. Some students may say that the white numbers cannot be divided by two (by this, they mean without a remainder).

Extension

As an introduction to number patterns, you may have students identify the rule for each of the following number sequences:

0, 2, 4, 6, ... (add two to each number)

1, 2, 4, 8, ... (double each number)

0, 1, 1, 2, 3, 5, 8, ... (add two consecutive numbers)

6, 11, 16, ... (add five to each number)

Students may also create their own number sequences.

Notes

Show the red, white, and blue strip. Ask students to look at the strip and write down two patterns they notice. With a partner, have them push the list to 5 or more items. Share as a class. All students should be able to contribute. Ask students how to predict the color of any number in the pattern if this does not come up in the discussion.

Relating the visual representation to the symbolic notation helps many students make sense of the formulas and how they are developed. Whenever possible in class discussion, ask students to explain the connections between representations explicitly.

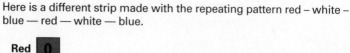

Patterns

Here is a different strip made with the repeating pattern red – white – blue — red — white — blue.

Any list of numbers that goes on forever is called a **sequence**.

3. How can you figure out the color in the red-white-blue sequence for 253,679?

One way to "see" a pattern is to use dots to represent numbers. For example, the red numbers from the red and white strip on page 1 can be drawn like this:

Dot Pattern:						
Pattern Number:	0	1	2	3	4	5

Below each dot pattern is a pattern number. The pattern number tells you where you are in a sequence. (Notice that the pattern number starts with 0, and there are no dots for pattern number 0.)

Pattern number 1 shows two dots, pattern number 2 shows four dots, and so on, assuming that the pattern continues building dots in the same way.

4. a. Look at the dot pattern for the red numbers. When the pattern number is 37, how many dots are there?

   b. Someone came up with the formula $R = 2n$ for the red numbers. What do you think R and n stand for?

   c. Does the formula work? Explain your answer.

Reaching All Learners

Advanced Learners

For problem 3, ask students to predict some larger numbers that are red. *What do they have in common? How can I use this to tell if a number is blue or white?*

Intervention

For problem 4, be sure students understand they are going back to the red and white odd-even pattern on page 1. If necessary, have students draw a new strip with only the even numbers.

English Language Learners

Discuss and illustrate the meaning of the word *sequence*.

Solutions and Samples

3. 253,679 is a blue number. Explanations will vary. Sample explanation:

   Red numbers are 0, 3, 6, and so on. These are multiples of three. White numbers are 1, 4, 7, and so on. These numbers are one more than multiples of three (or they have a remainder of 1 when divided by 3). Blue numbers are 2, 5, 8, and so on. These numbers are two more than multiples of 3 (or have a remainder of two when divided by three). To find out the color of 253,679, divide it by three and look at the remainder.

   $253{,}679 \div 3 = 84{,}559$ with remainder 2, so it is a blue number.

4. **a.** There are 74 dots. Strategies will vary. Some students may say that the pattern number shows the number of rows of two dots that are in the pattern. The 37th pattern number would have 37 rows of two dots, or 74 dots total.

   b. R stands for the number of red dots. The letter n stands for the pattern number.

   c. Yes, the formula works because the number of dots is double the pattern number. If students have difficulty with the direct formula $R = 2n$, you may want to start with a table and a word formula:

Pattern Number	Number of Dots
0	0
1	2
2	4
3	6

number of dots = 2 × pattern number

Hints and Comments

Materials

calculators, optional (one per student)

Overview

Students learn what a number sequence is. They figure out the color of a large number in a number sequence with a repeating color pattern. They also use a dot pattern to visualize the pattern of the numbers in the sequence.

About the Mathematics

It is important for students to understand that for this number strip, the first number in the sequence has pattern number 0 (the starting number). After one step, the pattern number is 1. So, even if the first number in the sequence is 1 (or 2, or any other number) the starting number is pattern number 0. This starting point is an important concept because this is the way in which formulas will be set up later in this section. Note: The dot pattern refers to the strip on page 1 of the Student Book.

Planning

You may want to have students work on problems 3 and 4 in small groups and then discuss their strategies as a class.

Comments About the Solutions

3. Students who use their calculators to answer this question will get the decimal remainder .666, which they may know is equal to $\frac{2}{3}$, so it has remainder 2.

4. If students have difficulty with direct formulas such as $R = 2n$, you may wish to review the ideas and notations involved. Make sure students realize that this problem is about the red numbers.

   a. Note that you can start the pattern number for a sequence anywhere. The important thing is for students to understand where the sequence starts. In this case, it starts with 0.

Notes

5b If students have trouble writing the formula, have them explain the formula for the even numbers again, focusing on the relationship between the pattern number and the number of dots. Ask what changes when we look at the odd numbers.

6a If students have difficulty using dots to explain the statement, ask what happens to the extra dot from each odd number when you add.

7 This problem emphasizes the importance of including the start number in recursive (NEXT-CURRENT) formulas.

You can represent the white numbers from the red-white strip on page 1 in their own pattern: 1, 3, 5, …

These numbers can be represented using a different dot pattern as shown below.

Dot Pattern:						
Pattern Number:	**0**	**1**	**2**	**3**	**4**	**5**

5. a. Now look at the pattern for the white numbers. How many dots are in pattern number 50?

   b. Write a formula for the white numbers.

Rule: ***"If you add two odd numbers, you get an even number."***

6. a. Use dots to explain the rule above.

   b. Make up some other rules like the one above, and use dots to explain them.

The sequence of even numbers {0, 2, 4, 6, 8 …} can be described by the formula:

$$\text{START number} = 0$$
$$\text{NEXT even number} = \text{CURRENT even number} + 2$$

You may have seen these "NEXT-CURRENT" formulas in previous *Mathematics in Context* units. They are more formally called **recursive formulas.**

7. a. Write a NEXT-CURRENT formula for the sequence of odd numbers

$$\{1, 3, 5, 7\}.$$

   b. Compare the formulas for even and odd numbers assuming that the pattern continues building dots in the same way. What is the same and what is different?

A formula such as those you found above for even and odd numbers is called a **direct formula.**

8. Why do you think these are called direct formulas?

Reaching All Learners

Intervention

For problem 6, some students may need to draw the dots for pairs of odd numbers to see how the two "extra" dots pair up. This can be done on transparencies; slide the dot patterns together to show how two extra dots make a pair.

Advanced Learners

For problem 6b, challenge advanced learners to make rules involving operations other than addition. Subtraction and multiplication work well here. Ask them to show how to use the dot pictures and the direct formula to justify their results.

Solutions and Samples

5. a. There are 101 dots in pattern number 50. Strategies will vary, depending on how students see the pattern.

If they see the pattern as having a dot missing in the upper right corner, the calculation is $2 \times 51 - 1 = 101$ dots

If they see the pattern as having an extra dot in the upper left corner, the calculation may be $2 \times 50 + 1 = 101$ dots

If the pattern is seen as two columns of dots, the calculation may be $50 + 51 = 101$

b. The formula depends on the strategy used for the solution to problem 5a. The following are possible formulas:

$W = 2n + 1$

$W = 2(n + 1) - 1$, or in words, "double the next pattern number, and subtract one."

$W = n + (n + 1)$

Some students may come up with a NEXT-CURRENT formula:

START number = 0

NEXT number = CURRENT number + 2

Ask for a direct formula as well.

6. a. Strategies will vary. One way to explain the rule is to turn the pattern for one of the white numbers upside down. The single dot "gap" now fits into the gap of the other pattern. Students might also say that the two odd numbers have single dots that can be paired.

b. Answers will vary. Other possible rules:

Add two evens, get an even.

Add an odd and an even, get an odd.

7. a. START number = 1

NEXT number = CURRENT number + 2

b. The NEXT-CURRENT formulas for odd and even numbers are similar since each step involves adding two. The formulas are different because they do not have the same starting number.

Hints and Comments

Materials

Student Activity Sheet 1, optional (one per student); graphing calculators, optional (one per student)

Overview

Students use patterns of numbers represented as dots to develop a formula. They also use dot patterns to explain why adding two odd numbers results in an even number. Students study a NEXT-CURRENT, or recursive, formula and compare formulas for even and odd numbers. They learn about direct formulas and what makes these formulas "direct."

About the Mathematics

An important aspect of creating formulas in all *Mathematics in Context* units is relating visual information to algebraic symbols. For example, the formulas $R = 2n$ and $W = 2n + 1$ can each be seen in the way the dot patterns are arranged.

Direct formulas are used to find any term in a sequence, provided you know its position in the sequence. Recursive formulas are used to describe the successive term with regard to the current term. The focus of a recursive formula is on the change between successive terms.

Planning

After discussing the recursive formula on page 3, you may want students to work on problems 7 and 8 as a whole-class activity. Some graphing calculators let you create a sequence of numbers using either direct or recursive formulas. You can use the **Student Activity Sheet 1** to investigate sequences with a calculator. If time is a concern, this activity may be omitted or assigned as homework.

Comments About the Solutions

7. Problem 7 is critical because it is the first time in this unit that students use a recursive formula.

8. You might remind students that they used direct formulas on the previous page when they were working with pattern numbers.

8. Sample explanation:

They are called direct formulas because you can find out the even (red) or odd (white) number directly, given only the pattern number. You don't have to proceed step-by-step starting from the beginning of the pattern.

A Patterns

Look again at the red–white–blue sequence from page 2.

9 Be sure students transition back to the red, white, and blue pattern.

9a Ask students to list the first few red numbers and draw the dot patterns for each. It will help students see the patterns if they draw the dots in groups of three. Ask why this is reasonable to do. Students can then write the pattern numbers under the dot representation. The pattern numbers count (starting at 0) the red numbers. Repeat the process for blue and white numbers.

9d and e Many students have trouble completing the chart. Discuss part **d** as a class. Focus on how the dots combine to make groups of 3. Enter information from this problem into the chart to start 9e.

9. **a.** Represent the red, white, and blue numbers using dot patterns similar to the dot patterns shown on pages 2 and 3.

   b. Write a NEXT-CURRENT formula and a direct formula for the sequence of red numbers. State where your sequence begins in both cases.

   c. Do the same for the sequences of white numbers and blue numbers.

   d. If you add a white number to a blue number, do you always get a red number? Use dots to explain your answer.

   e. Copy the chart in your notebook and complete it for all combinations of colors.

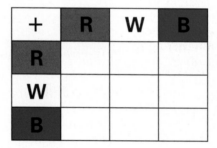

+	R	W	B
R			
W			
B			

Assessment Pyramid

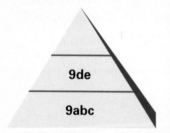

9de

9abc

Assesses ability to represent simple patterns using diagrams and recursive and direct formulas.

Reaching All Learners

Intervention

For problem 9b, ask students how they can get the next few numbers in each sequence. How are they doing this? Most students are adding three, which leads to the recursive formula. How could they find the 100th one? Some students may need help connecting the pattern number to the number of groups of three in the dot pattern.

Intervention

If students have trouble filling in the chart for problem 9e, ask them to use the dot patterns to show what happens to the "extra" dots when different colors are combined. What color has the same combination of dots as the sum? Using some specific examples helps.

Solutions and Samples

9. a.

Red:

$$\begin{array}{cccc} & \bullet\bullet\bullet & \bullet\bullet\bullet & \bullet\bullet\bullet \\ \bullet\bullet\bullet & \bullet\bullet\bullet & \bullet\bullet\bullet & \bullet\bullet\bullet \\ 0 & 1 & 2 & 3 \end{array}$$

White:

$$\begin{array}{cccc} & & & \circ \\ & & \circ\circ\circ & \circ\circ\circ \\ \circ & \circ\circ\circ & \circ\circ\circ & \circ\circ\circ \\ 0 & 1 & 2 & 3 \end{array}$$

Blue:

$$\begin{array}{cccc} & & \bullet\bullet\bullet & \bullet\bullet\bullet \\ & \bullet\bullet\bullet & \bullet\bullet\bullet & \bullet\bullet\bullet \\ \bullet\bullet & \bullet\bullet\bullet & \bullet\bullet\bullet & \bullet\bullet\bullet \\ 0 & 1 & 2 & 3 \end{array}$$

b. Red NEXT-CURRENT formula:
START number = 0
NEXT red = CURRENT red + 3
Direct formula: $R = 3n$ (n starts at zero) or
$R = 3(n - 1)$ (n starts at 1)

c. White NEXT-CURRENT formula:
START number = 1
NEXT white = CURRENT white + 3
Direct formula: $W = 3n + 1$ (n starts at zero) or
$W = 3(n - 1) + 1$ (n starts at 1)

Blue NEXT-CURRENT formula:
START number = 2
NEXT blue = CURRENT blue + 3
Direct formula: $B = 3n + 2$ (n starts at zero) or
$B = 3(n - 1) + 2$ (n starts at 1)

d. Yes. One way to show this is to turn a white pattern upside down and fit the single dot for the white number with the two single dots for the blue number. The resulting pattern has rows of three dots, a red number. Students might also say that there is one single dot in a white number and two single dots in a blue. When put together, they form a complete row of three dots.

$$\begin{array}{c} \circ \\ \circ\circ\circ \\ \circ\circ\circ \end{array} + \begin{array}{c} \bullet\bullet \\ \bullet\bullet\bullet \end{array} = ?$$

e.

+	R	W	B
R	R	W	B
W	W	B	R
B	B	R	W

Hints and Comments

Overview

Students again use the red-white-blue sequence, which they represent using dot patterns and for which they write NEXT-CURRENT and recursive formulas. They investigate the results of adding combinations of red, white, and blue numbers.

Planning

Students may work on problem 9 in small groups. This problem may also be assigned as homework. Be sure to discuss students' answers in class.

Comments About the Solutions

9. a. You may give students the hint that they should use rows of three in all of their dot patterns for red, white, and blue numbers.

b.–c. It is not necessary that n means the same thing in all three formulas, but students should be able to explain how it is used in each formula.

d. A more abstract explanation is possible using the formulas. Note, however, that you cannot use the same n twice ($3n + 1 + 3n + 2$ is incorrect or incomplete). This is because $3n + 1$ and $3n + 2$ represent consecutive numbers; we must be able to represent any white number and any blue number.

To do this on a formal level is probably too difficult for most students. Consider $3n + 1$ to be any white number and $3m + 2$ to be any blue number. Their sum is:

$(3n + 1) + (3m + 2)$

$= 3n + 3m + 3$

$= 3(n + m + 1)$

The number, $3(n + m + 1)$, is a multiple of three and the red numbers are the sequence of the multiples of three. So, $3(n + m + 1)$ must be a red number (other than zero).

e. Students should fill in each cell with R, W, or B.

A Patterns

Notes

Give students a minute to study the V-patterns. Then ask what pattern number should replace the question mark for the V with 17 dots.

Ask students to explain. Look for different ways students visualize the pattern—two equal arms plus the base dot, two unequal arms, or pairs horizontally with the unpaired dot at the bottom. Be sure they connect the pattern number to features of the dot diagram.

V- and W-Formations

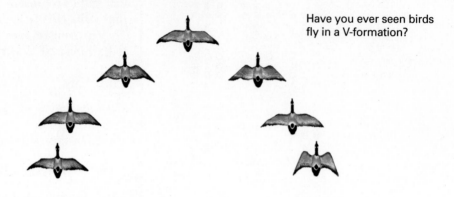

Have you ever seen birds fly in a V-formation?

You can make a sequence of V-patterns using dots. The first four are shown below.

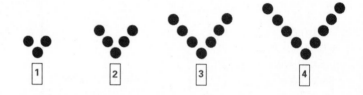

Here is a V-number that uses 17 dots.

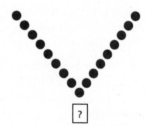

Reaching All Learners

Extension

Students investigate V- and W-patterns on the next several pages. It might be interesting to ask, *Which letters of the alphabet can you use to make patterns? Where would the points of growth be for each letter?*

Hints and Comments

Overview

Students investigate V-patterns in the context of birds flying in a V-formation. There are no problems on this page for students to solve.

Note that with the V- and W-formations the first pattern number is 1, and not 0, as in the dot patterns. The pattern numbers are shown in different ways throughout the unit. This was done deliberately to help students to get accustomed to different representations.

Technology

The applet Spotting Numbers, found at http://mic.hrw.com, can be used to demonstrate how various dot patterns build from step to step.

A Patterns

Notes

10c If students do not recognize that all the V-numbers are odd, have them look again at pattern on page 5. Ask how many dots are in each, and what those numbers have in common. How is this shown in the dot diagram?

11 Students may benefit from friendly reminders to write the coefficient in front of the variable in their formulas.

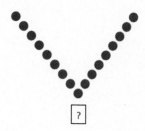

10. a. What is the pattern number of this drawing?

    b. How many dots are in pattern number 85?

    c. Is it possible to make a V-pattern with 35,778 dots? Explain why or why not.

    d. Write a direct formula to describe the number of dots in any V-pattern. $V = ?$

The letter n is usually used in direct formulas to denote pattern numbers.

For some patterns n starts with 0 and sometimes with 1. It may start with other numbers as well.

11. If you haven't already done so, write your V-pattern formula using the letter n.

Squadrons of airplanes sometimes fly in a W-formation.

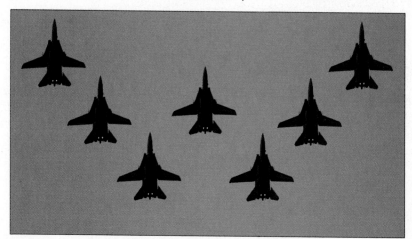

Assessment Pyramid

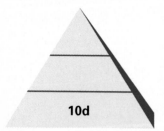

10d

Assesses ability to write a direct formula to describe the sequence of odd numbers.

Reaching All Learners

Extension

You may ask students to write a NEXT-CURRENT formula to describe the number of dots in any V-pattern.

Intervention

For problems 10a and b, it might help students if they look for a relationship between the pattern number and the number of dots in the pattern. This relationship can be seen in different ways, depending on how the pattern is split. The technique of splitting the pattern is also used in the unit *Building Formulas*.

Solutions and Samples

10. a. The pattern number is 8. Sample strategy:

There are two equal groups of dots with one connector dot in the middle. The number of dots in either of the equal groups is the pattern number. In this case, the pattern number is 8.

b. 171 dots ($2 \times 85 + 1 = 171$ dots)

c. No. Strategies will vary. Sample strategy:

The total number of dots is always odd. Since 35,778 is an even number, no such pattern exists.

d. Formulas may vary. Sample formulas:

$V = 2n + 1$

$V = n + (n + 1)$

In each case, n starts at 1.

11. See answer to question 10d.

Hints and Comments

Overview

Students explore the relationship between the pattern number and the number of dots in the pattern. They then write a direct formula to describe the number of dots in any pattern.

About the Mathematics

V-numbers are really just another name for the sequence of odd numbers, although the sequence of odd numbers starts at 1, and here the V-numbers start at 3.

Planning

Students may work on problems 10 and 11 in small groups. You may want to discuss students' answers as a class.

Comments About the Solutions

10. c. It is possible to formally solve the equation $2n + 1 = 35,778$ and discover that n is not a whole number. However, at this point, it is unlikely that students will come up with this strategy.

d. As in problems 10a. and b, the formula may be written in different ways, depending on how students split the pattern.

11. The starting number for a pattern is very important. When reading a formula for a pattern, students should always ask, "Where does n start?" and when writing a formula for a pattern, they should always give this information.

Notes

12b Students can associate the question "What comes next?" or "How do I get to the next one from the current one?" with the NEXT-CURRENT or recursive formula. Some students may need to be reminded to include the start number with the recursive formula.

12d Some students will focus on the relationship between the pattern number and the corresponding entry in the pattern. Other students will think about how many times they add a certain number (here, 4) to the starting value. Some will connect the recursive formula to the direct formula. These types of connections will continue to develop throughout the unit. Students benefit from hearing other approaches during class discussion.

Look at the following sequence of W-patterns.

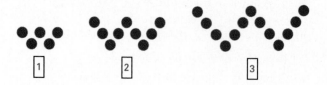

12. **a.** Copy and complete this chart for the W-patterns.

Number of Dots	5					
Pattern Number	1	2	3	4	5	6

b. Write a NEXT-CURRENT formula for the number of dots in the W-pattern sequence.

c. How many dots are in pattern number 16?

d. Find a direct formula to describe the number of dots in any W-pattern. Then use your formula to find the number of dots in pattern number 25.

Jessie compared the W-patterns to the V-patterns. She said, "W is double V minus one."

13. **a.** What did Jessie mean? Use dot patterns to explain her statement.

b. Explain Jessie's statement using direct formulas for $W = \ldots$ and $V = \ldots$

The Williams Pie Company wants to display a big **"W"** with orange light bulbs on a billboard. They order 200 light bulbs.

14. If they place the light bulbs in a W-pattern, how many bulbs would there be in the largest W they can make?

Assessment Pyramid

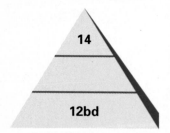

Write recursive and direct formulas for an arithmetic sequence.

Use a formula to find a location in the pattern.

Reaching All Learners

Hands-On Learning

For problem 13a, it will help visual learners if you make two corresponding V-patterns on overhead transparencies so students can show how two dots overlap as they slide the Vs together to make the W.

Intervention

In problem 13b, if some students have trouble using the direct formula, guide them through the process step-by-step. *What do you get when you double the V formula? Subtract 1? How does this compare to the formula for the W-pattern?*

Solutions and Samples

12. a.

Number of Dots	5	9	13	17	21	25
Pattern Number	1	2	3	4	5	6

b. START number = 5
NEXT W-number = CURRENT W-number + 4

c. There are 65 dots in pattern 16.

d. Direct formulas may vary. Sample formulas:
$W = 4n + 1$, n starts at 1

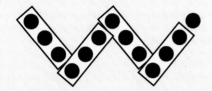

For this W-pattern, the pattern number n is 3. The number of dots is always 4 times the pattern number plus one more: $4n + 1$ dots.

$W = 2n + 2(n + 1) - 1$

The number of dots is always: two groups of dots equal to the pattern number, $2n$; two groups of dots with one more than the pattern number, $2(n + 1)$; but one of the dots has been counted twice, so we must subtract one. So the formula is $W = 2n + 2(n + 1) - 1$.

Pattern 25 has 101 dots. Students should use their own formulas to check. One example using the formula $W = 4n + 1$:
$W = 4 \times 25 + 1$
$W = 100 + 1$
$W = 101$

13. a. She meant that each W has one less than twice as many dots as a *V* with the same pattern number. If you put two V's next to each other, one dot overlaps.

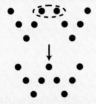

b. Answers will vary. Sample explanation:

The W-pattern always has one less dot than two V-patterns side by side. If one V-pattern has $2n + 1$ dots ($V = 2n + 1$), then a W-pattern has $2n + 1 + 2n + 1 - 1$ dots, or
$W = 2(2n + 1) - 1$
$W = 4n + 2 - 1$
$W = 4n + 1$

Hints and Comments

Overview

Students investigate W-patterns in the context of airplanes flying in a W-formation. They write a NEXT-CURRENT formula and a direct formula to describe the number of dots in a W-pattern sequence.

Students compare a V-pattern to a W-pattern. Then they find the largest W-pattern that can be made with 200 dots.

Planning

Students may work on problems 12, 13 and 14 in small groups. Problem 14 may also be assigned as homework.

Comments About the Solutions

12. c. Answers can be found by drawing and counting the numbers of dots, by using the recursive relationship, or by trying to find a direct formula for the number of dots in the nth W-pattern. Because the 16th pattern has 65 dots, drawing is tedious. Using the recursive relationship may also take a great deal of time.

13. a. You may wish to have students make tables showing the W- and V-patterns and use reasoning to explain Jesse's statement.

b. This question is meant to be an initial exposure to manipulating expressions symbolically. Some students may find this easy, while other students may struggle. This concept will be revisited in Section B. Some students may remember this type of problem from *Building Formulas*. It is not recommended that you teach the distributive property at this point in the unit.

14. This problem enables you to see how well students can identify patterns either in number sequences or pictures and whether or not they can create formulas for them. Look for a variety of strategies as students share their responses. This problem is going in the opposite direction (finding n), so many students will need to think about a strategy for solving this.

n	$W = 4n + 1$
20	81
40	161
50	201
49	197

14. There would be 197 bulbs. Strategies will vary. Students may use a trial-and-error method with the formula to try to get close to 200.

Notes

Students read and discuss the Summary reviewing how number sequences can be represented. Then they use the Check Your Work problems as self-assessment. The answers to these problems are also provided in the Student Book.

1 If students are having difficulty, you may remind them that *n* starts at 0, not 1. The start number for the recursive rule is not necessarily the same as the pattern number.

A Patterns

Summary

Number strips and dot patterns can illustrate sequences of numbers. You can use formulas to describe sequences and to find numbers later in the sequence. Here is an example where the dots continue to build in the same way.

Dot Pattern:				
Pattern Number:	0	1	2	3

A NEXT-CURRENT formula or *recursive* formula has two parts: a start value and a rule for finding each "next" value. A recursive formula for the number of dots in the dot pattern above is:

START number = 1
NEXT number = CURRENT number + 3

A *direct formula* uses *n* to indicate the pattern number. If *D* stands for the number of dots, a direct formula for the pattern above is:

$D = 3n + 1$, where *n* starts with 0.

Check Your Work

1. James wrote the direct formula $D = 1 + n + n + n$ for the dot pattern in the Summary. Show whether or not James's formula is correct.

Reaching All Learners

Study Skills

To help students summarize similarities and differences between direct and recursive formulas, have students divide their paper in three columns. List information and attributes of recursive formulas on the left, of direct formulas on the right, and things they have in common in the center. (This is like a Venn diagram in table form.) Have students share ideas in their groups to expand their lists, then discuss as a class. Lists can be combined into a class list and/or they can be posted.

Solutions and Samples

Answers to Check Your Work

1. James's formula is correct. One way to show this is to point out that each pattern has 3 rows of n dots, plus one on top: $3n + 1$.

Hints and Comments

Overview

Students complete the Check Your Work and For Further Reflection problems.

Planning

You may want to discuss students' answers to the Check Your Work problems in class. After students finish Section A, you may assign as homework appropriate activities from the Additional Practice section, located on Student Book page 39.

Notes

2b Starting with a different pattern number changes the direct formula. Ask students to explain why this is true.

3a Monitor students work to be sure they group dots by fives, since 5 is added each time.

4 You may want to share sequences students make, or make a poster where students can add theirs if they wish.

For Further Reflection

Reflective questions are meant to summarize and discuss important concepts.

Look again at the dot pattern of page 3.

Dot Pattern:	•	• • • •	• • • • • •	• • • • • • • •	• • • • • • • • • •	• • • • • • • • • • • •
Pattern Number:	0	1	2	3	4	5

David came up with the formula $W = 2n + 1$ for this pattern.
Cindy found the direct formula $W = 2(n + 1) - 1$

2. **a.** Are both formulas correct? Why or why not?

   b. How would David's formula change if the first pattern number is 1 instead of 0?

3. **a.** Make a sequence of dot patterns for the direct formula $D = 5n + 2$, where n starts at 0.

   b. Write a NEXT-CURRENT formula for the sequence.

4. **a.** Make up your own dot-pattern sequence.

   b. Write a direct formula and a NEXT-CURRENT formula for your sequence.

5. **Reflect** What is one advantage and one disadvantage of a recursive formula compared to a direct formula?

For Further Reflection

Can every sequence of numbers be represented by a dot pattern? Why or why not?

Reaching All Learners

Study Skills

Ask students to review the different patterns in Section A. As a summary, ask students to write directions for finding a recursive formula for a given pattern. Then write directions for finding the direct formula for a given pattern. Ask. *What connections are there between the two types of formulas for the same pattern?*

Solutions and Samples

2. a. Yes, both formulas are correct. Your explanation may differ from the ones presented here. If that is the case, discuss it with a classmate. Sample explanations.

- If you fill in number 1, 2, 3, 4, etc. in both formulas, you get the same dot pattern.
- $2(n+1) - 1 = 2n + 2 - 1 = 2n + 1$.

b. A table may help you find the answer for this problem.

Pattern Number	Number of Dots
1	1
2	3
3	5
4	7
5	9
6	11

David's formula would change into $W = 2n - 1$ or $W = 2(n+1) - 3$.

3. a. Students' dot-pattern sequences will vary. Sample dot pattern:

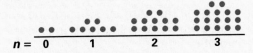

b. START NUMBER = 2
NEXT = CURRENT + 5

4. a. There are many possible patterns. Discuss your pattern with a classmate. Here is a sample pattern.

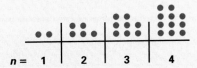

b. Make sure your direct formula and your "NEXT-CURRENT" formula correspond with your sequence. Fill in $n = 3, 4, 5$, etc. to check.

A direct formula for the sample sequence of 4a is: $D = 3n - 1$; n starts at 1. (D represents the number of dots.)

A NEXT CURRENT formula is
NEXT = CURRENT + 3; START number is 2

Hints and Comments

Overview

Students use the Check Your Work problems as self-assessment. The answers to these problems are also provided in the Student Book.

5. An advantage of a NEXT-CURRENT formula is that it is often easier to make. You only have to look at the start number and the constant increase or decrease.

A disadvantage to a NEXT-CURRENT formula is that it does not immediately give you the number of dots for any pattern number in the sequence. You have to generate all of the elements before the one in which you are interested in order to know its value.

If you found other advantages or disadvantages, discuss those in class.

For Further Reflection

No. Dot patterns work well for whole number patterns. However, patterns involving decimals, fractions, negative numbers, and so on, are difficult to represent with dots.

Section Focus

This section introduces the concept of *arithmetic sequence*. Students use repeated addition and subtraction to generate other terms in a given sequence.

Pacing and Planning

Day 4: Constant Increase/Decrease		Student pages 10 and 11
INTRODUCTION	Problems 1 and 2	Investigate the step-by-step increase on a number strip for an arithmetic sequence.
CLASSWORK	Problems 3–6	Write direct and recursive formulas for an increasing and decreasing arithmetic sequence.
HOMEWORK	Problem 7	Create a number sequence with a pattern that is or is not an arithmetic sequence.

Day 5: Adding and Subtracting Strips		Student pages 12–15
INTRODUCTION	Problem 8	Combine the number strips of the odd and even numbers to form a new number strip.
CLASSWORK	Problems 9–13	Investigate adding and subtracting the number sequences and the expressions that represent the sequences.
HOMEWORK	Problems 14–16	Formalize the process for adding and subtracting the expressions that represent the sequences.

Day 6: Pyramids		Student pages 15–17
INTRODUCTION	Review homework.	Review homework from Day 5.
CLASSWORK	Problems 17–19	Make number strips and write direct formulas to represent the numbers of vertices, faces, and edges in a sequence of pyramids.
HOMEWORK	Problem 20	Demonstrate that Euler's formula applies to a sequence of prisms.

Day 7: Summary		Student pages 18 and 19
INTRODUCTION	Check Your Work	Student self-assessment: Create, extend, and analyze arithmetic sequences.
ASSESSMENT	Quiz 1	Assessment of Section A and B Goals
HOMEWORK	For Further Reflection	Investigate the validity of Euler's formula.

Additional Resources: *Algebra Tools*, Additional Practice, Section B, Student Book pages 40 and 41

Materials

Student Resources

No resources required

Teachers Resources

No resources required

Student Materials

No materials required

* See Hints and Comments for optional materials

Learning Lines

In an arithmetic sequence, the next numbers in the sequence are generated by a constant increase or decrease. Students investigate the step-by-step increase/decrease on number strips and they identify if a sequence is an arithmetic one or not. In case of arithmetic sequences, students will then demonstrate their ability to extend an arithmetic sequence and write recursive and direct formulas to represent them.

Students add and subtract number strips and expressions for arithmetic sequences to generate new arithmetic sequences. Students start to combine the number strips of the odd and even numbers to form a new number strip. Then they investigate adding and subtracting the number sequences and the expressions that represent the sequences. Students will find that the constant increase for the new sequence is the sum of the increases for the two original sequences. Students then combine the algebraic expressions that represent the sequences to form the expression for the new sequence.

In this section, Euler's formula is used as an example of combining sequences: students make number strips and write direct formulas to represent the number of vertices, faces, and edges in a sequence of pyramids and combine the strips and expressions to form Euler's formula.

Models

Number strips help to visualize sequences and operations between sequences.

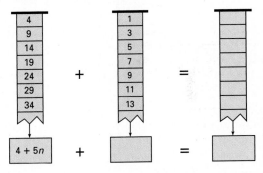

At the End of this Section: Learning Outcomes

Students identify and extend an arithmetic sequence, and write recursive and direct formulas to represent an arithmetic sequence. Students will also add and subtract number sequences and the corresponding expressions.

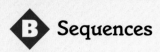
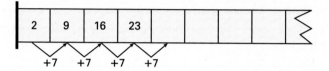

Sequences

Constant Increase/Decrease

A sequence that has a constant increase or decrease is called an **arithmetic sequence**. Here is an example of an arithmetic sequence. The jagged right end indicates that the strip continues forever.

1b Some students have trouble seeing that numbers that are two more than a multiple of 7 are on the strip. Some students will continue to add 7 until they get to 100. Others will work backwards. Others will use a guess-and-check strategy. Ask students to present different strategies before going on to 2c and 2d.

2b Ask students to show their work. How are they using the expression to get the terms in the sequence?

3a Monitor students as they work to see they understand there are three steps from 41 to 65, although there are only two blanks.

1. **a.** Write four more numbers as they appear on the strip.

   b. Will the number 100 be on the number strip? How do you know?

   c. How about the number 200?

   d. Write a large number that will never appear on the strip. How do you know for sure that it will never appear?

Jorge came up with the expression $2 + 7n$ for the number strip shown on this page.

2. **a.** Where does n start in Jorge's expression?

   b. Use the expression to find the next three numbers on the strip.

Here is a number strip showing a different arithmetic sequence.

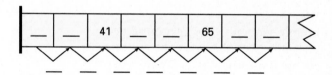

3. **a.** Find the missing numbers on the strip.

   b. Write a recursive formula for this number strip.

   c. Write an expression for this number strip. Let n start at zero.

Assessment Pyramid

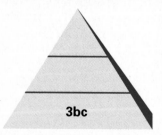

3bc

Write recursive formulas and direct expressions for an arithmetic sequence.

Reaching All Learners

Vocabulary Building

The term *arithmetic* can be used as a noun. It can also be used as an adjective, as it is in "arithmetic sequence." The pronunciation changes depending on the usage: uh-RITH-muh-TIC for the noun and AIR-ith-MET-ic for the adjective. Connect the term *expression* to direct formula.

Making Connections

With problem 2b, students might start by substituting 0 for n, then 1 for n, and so on, to find that the three numbers they are looking for are $n = 4$, $n = 5$, and $n = 6$. Discuss the difference between a (direct) formula like $dots = 2 + 7n$ and an *expression* like $2 + 7n$ with your students.

Solutions and Samples

1. a. 30, 37, 44, 51

b. Yes. The number minus 2 must be divisible by seven. $100 - 2 = 98$, which is divisible by seven.

Some students might extend the table. Other students might realize that when you add seven each time, you add the multiples of seven as well. Therefore, from the next entry (30), you may add 70 to get to 100. Still others might use a direct expression for the strip, $2 + 7n$ (n starts at 0) and try to find when $2 + 7n = 100$. Here is an example using a reverse arrow string.

$$100 \xrightarrow{-2} 98 \xrightarrow{\div 7} 14$$

So 100 is the 14th pattern number.

c. No, 200 will not be on the number strip because every number on the strip is two more than a multiple of seven. The number $200 = 2 + 198$, and $198 \div 7$ is not a whole number. Alternatively, students can go to a number they are sure is on the strip (such as 170) and add groups of seven from there.

d. For example 500 is not on the strip. Any number that is not two more than a multiple of seven will not be on the strip. For example, a student might say that 500 is not on the strip because 7×70 is 490, which increases to 497 and 504, and adding two produces 492, 499, and 506. So the closest you get to 500 is 499. Students might also subtract two from 500 and find that 498 is not divisible by seven.

2 a. In Jorge's expression, n starts at 0.

b. $2 + 7 \times 4 = 30$
$2 + 7 \times 5 = 37$
$2 + 7 \times 6 = 44$

3. a.

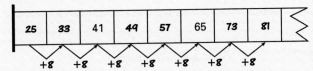

Students might reason that the difference between 41 and 65 is 24. Since this must be added over three steps, each step must add eight. This strategy can be used to find numbers to the left and right of 41 and 65.

b. START number = 25
NEXT number = CURRENT number + 8

c. $25 + 8n$; n starts at 0

Hints and Comments

Overview

Students learn what arithmetic sequences are and study an example from a number strip. They explore ways to find out whether a number will or will not be in a given sequence, and they use an expression and a NEXT-CURRENT formula to describe the sequence.

About the Mathematics

In calculating the numbers on the strip using the expression $2 + 7n$, students should follow the correct order of operations: they first carry out the multiplication (times seven) and then add (plus two).

A number sequence that is not specified by some condition has an infinite number of "next" terms. For example, 1, 3, 5, … could have 7, or the sequence could begin again, or it could reverse, or… The condition can be given by some mathematical information (arithmetic sequence or constant increase) or geometric pattern.

Planning

Be sure students understand what is meant by an arithmetic sequence. Arithmetic sequences are formed by repeatedly adding or subtracting the same number at each step. In the sequence {4, 7, 10, 13, 16, …}, the starting number is 4, and the difference between any two consecutive terms is three. In the sequence {10, 8, 6, 4, 2, …}, the starting number is 10, and each number is two less than the previous number. The sequence {1, 3, 6, 10, 15, …} has a pattern of increase (add 2, add 3, add 4, add 5, …), but this is not an arithmetic sequence.

Students may work on problems 1, 2, and 3 in small groups. You may want to discuss students' answers as a whole-class activity. Be sure to discuss their answers before proceeding.

Technology

The MiC Website, http://mic.hrw.com, has several applets that can be used for additional practice; for example, Number Strips, and Spotting Numbers.

Comments About the Solutions

1. a. and **b.**
Strategies in which students add on to numbers they are sure of (such as 100 or 170) are encouraged, since this promotes an understanding of both the formula $2 + 7n$ and the fact that the $7n$ in the expression means "increase n by 1, increase the pattern by 7."

2. Problem 2 is critical for evaluating students' ability to use expressions to describe arithmetic sequences.

Notes

Instead of adding a number at each step, some arithmetic sequences subtract a number at each step.

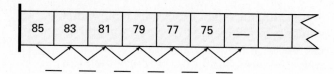

85	83	81	79	77	75	—	—

4. **a.** What is the decrease in this sequence?

   b. Write an expression for this number strip. Let n start at 0.

   c. Explain the difference between a (direct) formula and an expression.

   d. How many steps does it take to get to the first negative number in this strip?

5. Find an expression for the arithmetic sequence in the number strip drawn below. Let n start at 0 in your expression. You may copy the strip in your notebook and fill in the missing numbers first if you want to.

$3\frac{3}{4}$	$3\frac{1}{2}$		3		$2\frac{1}{2}$	$2\frac{1}{4}$	

6. Write the first five numbers in each of the sequences described by the following expressions. For each sequence, n starts at zero.

   a. $4 - 3n$

   b. $2\frac{1}{2} + \frac{1}{2}n$

   c. $5n - 10$

   d. $12n$

Many sequences are not arithmetic. Some involve multiplication and division.

7. **a.** Design a sequence that has a pattern or regularity but is not an arithmetic sequence.

   b. Describe the regularity in your sequence.

6 You may want to do 6a as a whole class. Students can then do the others on their own or in groups. Some students find 6d confusing because it looks different from the others. Remind them to see what happens if $n = 0$, then $n = 1$, etc. as they did in the previous examples. You may need to review order of operations here.

7 Share examples as a class. Have students predict the next few numbers for each pattern and describe the pattern verbally. Students enjoy exploring each others' patterns.

Assessment Pyramid

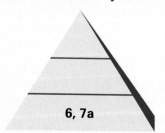

6, 7a

Generate a sequence from the formula.

Understand arithmetic sequences.

Reaching All Learners

Accommodation

It may help some students if you prepare a grid with $n = 0$, $n = 1$, etc. across the top and the formula on the left. Students can show the arithmetic sentence with the appropriate substitution for n in the corresponding box, then simplify.

Advanced Students

Challenge advanced students to write formulas for as many of the class examples from problem 7 as they can.

Vocabulary Building

Some students aren't sure of the meaning of the term *regularity*. Help them develop the meaning from the root word.

Solutions and Samples

4. a. There is a constant decrease of two.

b. $85 - 2n$; n starts at 0. One way to create this expression is to first fill in the spaces below the arrows. These are filled in with -2 so the expression is:
START number $+ (-2n)$, or $85 - 2n$.

c. A direct formula has the form of an equation, like *number of dots* $= 5 + 3n$. You can find numbers of dots for any n. The part of the previous formula, $5 + 3n$, is usually called an *expression* and is not an equation. It is written without an equal sign.

d. It takes 43 steps. Sample strategy: I started with 85, and with each step I subtracted two. I had to subtract at least 86 times to end up in the negative numbers. Since each number decreases by two, I only needed to divide 86 by 2 to get the number of steps needed (43). So 43 steps are needed to reach a negative number.

5. The constant *decrease* for this number strip is $\frac{1}{4}$. An expression is $3\frac{3}{4} - \frac{1}{4}n$, where n starts at 0.

6. a. $4, 1, -2, -5, -8$

b. $2\frac{1}{2}, 3, 3\frac{1}{2}, 4, 4\frac{1}{2}$

c. $-10, -5, 0, 5, 10$

d. $0, 12, 24, 36, 48$

7. a. Answers will vary. Sample response:
6, 12, 24, 48, 96 …

b. Answers will vary, depending on the sequence students create for problem 7a. The regularity of the sample sequence in part **a** is that the next number is the previous number times two.

Hints and Comments

Overview

Students use two number strips to find direct formulas and expressions. They learn that an arithmetic sequence may involve decrease as well as increase. Students create a number sequence that is not an arithmetic sequence and describe its regularity. Students also find a series of terms of sequences for which the expressions are given.

About the Mathematics

Arithmetic sequences can have a constant increase or a constant decrease. An example of an expression for an increase is $S + 2n$, while an expression for a decrease is $S - 2n$ (n starts at 0; S is the starting number of the sequence). A recursive formula for an increase is
NEXT *number* = CURRENT *number* + 2; START number = S.

A recursive formula for a decrease is
NEXT *number* = CURRENT *number* − 2; START number = S.

Non-arithmetic sequences that involve negative numbers are investigated. Direct formulas are used to generate a variety of sequences.

Comments About the Solutions

4. The sequence involves decrease instead of increase. Alternatively, it may be described in terms of adding a negative number in each step.

b. You may wish to take the time to talk about the expression $85 - 2n$. The 85 indicates where the sequence starts, while the n indicates how many groups of two to subtract from 85.

c. Be sure to discuss with your students the difference between a formula and an expression.

6. For each sequence, students should fill in 0, 1, 2, 3, 4, and 5 for n and calculate the corresponding terms. To be successful with this problem, students must have the ability to work with negative numbers and fractions.

7. a. The NEXT-CURRENT formula for the example given in the solutions column would be:
START *number* = 6
NEXT *number* = CURRENT *number* × 2

This is called a *geometric sequence*. A geometric sequence involves multiplying by a constant at every step, while an arithmetic sequence has a constant addition (or subtraction) at every step.

b. Students may describe the regularity in words, rather than with a mathematical expression.

B Sequences

Notes

8 The fourth number can be found by adding the fourth even number to the fourth odd number; the fifth number can be found by adding the fifth even number to the fifth odd number; and so on.

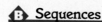

Adding and Subtracting Strips

Larry's favorite number strip is the sequence of odd numbers. He decides to add his number strip of odd numbers to the strip of even numbers.

Even

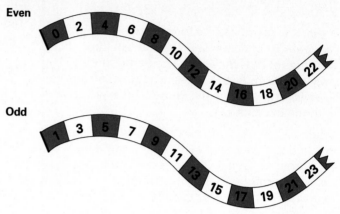

Odd

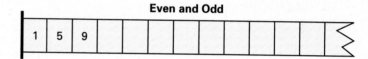

Here are the first three numbers of the resulting sequence:

8. Copy the number strip above and find the next nine numbers in the new sequence.

There is a connection between the W-patterns shown and the new number strip.

9. What is that connection?

Reaching All Learners

Accommodation

For some students you may want to prepare sheets with the strips that can be finished for problems such as 8, 11c, 14, and 15.

Solutions and Samples

8. 13, 17, 21, 25, 29, 33, 37, 41, and 45.

9. The number of dots in the W-pattern and the new number strip are the same with exception of the first number in the new number strip.

Hints and Comments

Overview

Students investigate the connection between W-patterns and numbers on a number strip. They combine number strips of even and odd numbers and find the numbers for the resulting sequence.

About the Mathematics

When numbers strips are added to or subtracted from one another, the sum or difference of the expressions for the number strips is equivalent to the expression that describes the numbers in the resulting strip. The informal combination of number strips leads to the concept of "adding like terms," which is discussed later in this section.

Planning

Students may work on problem 8 in small groups. Be sure to discuss students' answers.

Comments About the Solutions

9. You may want to remind students that they investigated W-patterns in Section A.

Extension

Students may make up their own arithmetic sequences, which they describe using a NEXT-CURRENT formula and an expression. They may represent them using number strips with blanks and ask other students to fill in the blanks and find the corresponding formula and expression.

You might want students to write recursive rules for their sequences.

Notes

10. **a.** Write an expression for each of the three numbers strips in problem 8. Let *n* start at zero.

   b. How can you use your expressions to check that the third sequence is the sum of the other two?

Compare these three number strips:

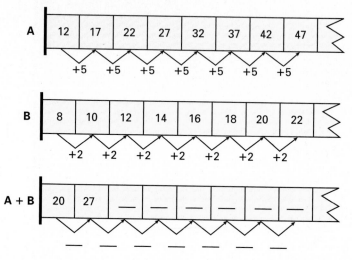

Number strips A and B are arithmetic sequences. The entries in the third strip, A + B, are formed by adding the numbers that appear in the same positions on strips A and B.

11a If students have difficulty, ask them how to tell if a sequence is arithmetic. Share responses to the question.

11. **a.** Without filling in the numbers for the strip A + B, you can show that it must be an arithmetic sequence. Explain how.

   b. Write expressions for the number strips A, B, and A + B.

   c. Make a number strip for A − B. Do the numbers form an arithmetic sequence? Explain why or why not.

   d. What expression corresponds to the number strip A − B?

11b and d Share responses. Students may notice that the formula for A + B is the same as the sum of the formulas for A and B. If not, you can ask if anyone sees a relationship. If students recognized this relationship, they may apply it in part **d.**

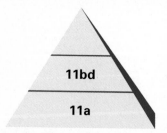
Reaching All Learners

Intervention

For problem 11c, you may want to remind students to investigate whether or not the new sequence shows increase or decrease.

Solutions and Samples

10. a. $2n$
   $2n + 1$
   $4n + 1$
   Where n starts at 0

b. Some students might be able to add the expressions $2n$ and $2n + 1$ to get $4n + 1$. Other students may check by substituting numbers into their expressions; for example, when $n = 5$:

   $2 \times 5 = 10$,
   $2 \times 5 + 1 = 11$,
   $4 \times 5 + 1 = 21$, and
   $10 + 11 = 21$

11. a. Explanations will vary. Sample explanation: Each term in strip A increases by five, and each term in strip B increases by two. If you combine these two strips, you have a strip in which each term increases by seven. Therefore, the new strip is still an arithmetic sequence with an increase of seven.

b. strip A: $12 + 5n$, where n starts at 0
   strip B: $8 + 2n$, where n starts at 0
   strip A + B: $20 + 7n$, where n starts at 0

c.

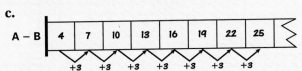

Yes, the numbers form an arithmetic sequence with an increase of three.

d. $4 + 3n$, where n starts at zero. Sample strategy: The expression for A is $12 + 5n$. The expression for B is $8 + 2n$.
   $$A - B = (12 + 5n) - (8 + 2n)$$
   $$= (12 - 8) + (5n - 2n)$$
   $$= 4 + 3n$$

Hints and Comments

Overview

Students use expressions to check the addition of number sequences. They investigate the sum of two number strips and reason about why the resulting number strip must be an arithmetic sequence. Students also learn how one number strip may be subtracted from another. They then write expressions to describe the two given strips and the strips resulting from adding and subtracting.

Planning

Students may work on problems 10 and 11 in small groups. Discuss students' solutions for both problems.

Comments About the Solutions

10. b. It is not necessary for students to be able to add the expressions formally. This skill will be taught later in this section.

11. d. Students may approach this problem in a way similar to that used in solving problem part **b**. However, in this case, they investigate the relationship between the direct expressions for strips A and B and that for strip A − B.

◆B Sequences

Notes

Strips C and D are two other number strips. The expression for strip C is 6 + 3n, and the expression for strip D is 4 + 5n. For both strips, n starts at zero.

Jim wants to make an expression for the strip C + D. First he makes the strips C and D. Then he adds the numbers on the two strips to get the numbers on strip C + D.

Then he makes the expression for the strip C + D.

12. Show the three steps in Jim's solution.

Gail thinks she knows a shorter way to come up with the expression.

13. a. What might Gail have in mind?

b. What is the expression for the number strip C − D?

14. Copy the three strips into your notebook. Fill in the missing numbers and write the expression for each number sequence.

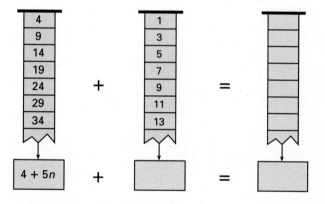

12 If students have difficulty, ask them to list the steps in Jim's solution. Then have them complete each step in order. Make strip C by listing the numbers, make strip D, then make the strip that shows the numbers in C + D. Last, write the expression for this combined strip.

13 Ask students to explain why it makes sense to add the formulas to get the formula for the sum of the two sequences. [The two starting numbers are added (6 + 4) and the increases for both sequences are added (3n + 5n).]

14 Students need to transition from the horizontal to the vertical representation of the sequences.

Reaching All Learners

Intervention

For problem 13b, if students have trouble seeing that the difference in the formulas gives the formula for the difference between the strips, have them write the new strip of numbers and its formula to verify this result.

Intervention

A few students may still need some assistance writing expressions for number strips. See if they can explain how the formula given for the first strip in problem 14 matches the numbers. Ask leading questions to help them find the formula for the second strip. The last expression for the sum can be derived from the number strip or by adding the first two expressions. Students can use this fact to check their formula.

Solutions and Samples

12.

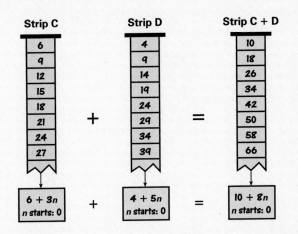

13. a. Gail might have thought to add the expressions for strips C and D:
$(6 + 3n) + (4 + 5n) = 10 + 8n$

b. The expression is $2 - 2n$.
Some students might subtract strip D from strip C:
strip C − D: $(6 + 3n) - (4 + 5n) = 2 - 2n$
Other students might make a strip as in problem 11 with the values for C − D, and then look for a pattern in this strip.

14.

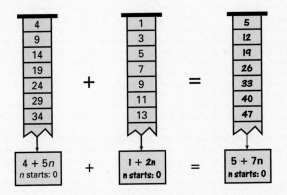

Hints and Comments

Overview

Students investigate more additions and subtractions of number sequences, using both number strips and expressions. They explore a shorter way to find the expression for the combination sequence by using only the expressions for the combined sequences.

Planning

Students may work on problems 12 and 13 in small groups. Be sure to discuss students' answers before they start working on problem 14. You may assign problem 14 for homework.

Comments About the Solutions

12. Students have to "translate" the expressions into number strips. The expressions indicate what the starting numbers of the strips are.

13. This problem is critical because students combine expressions for sequences rather than the sequences themselves. A discussion of different student strategies should allow students to see how this is done.

b. Encourage students to find this expression without making all three number strips. However, if they are having difficulty, they may use the number strips.

14. If students are able to write the expression for the combination sequence without filling in the third number strip, they may do so. You may want to make sure that students understand why and how the two expressions may be added.

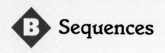
Notes

16 Check integer computation when students add and subtract these formulas. This can be a good place for a quick review.

17 Discuss this as a class. Students will see a variety of connections between the numbers and the drawings. It is interesting for students (and teacher) to see how many ways students visualize the connections.

15. Copy the three strips shown below. Fill in the missing numbers and write an expression for each number sequence.

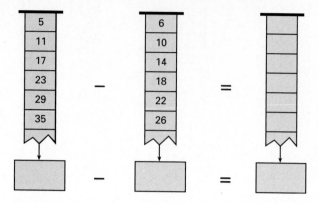

16. **a.** Write an expression for the sum of $17 + 5n$ and $13 - 7n$.

b. Write an expression for the difference of $17 + 5n$ and $13 - 7n$. Use number strips to show why your answer makes sense.

Pyramids

Billy is a glass artist who makes geometric shapes out of glass. Here is a sequence of his pyramids.

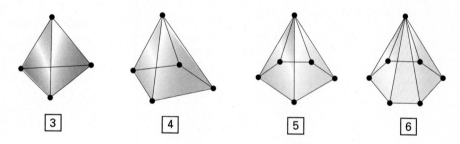

17. Explain the numbers below the pyramids.

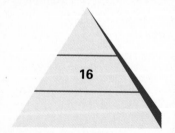
Reaching All Learners

Intervention

If combining the formulas without seeing the number strip in problem 16 is too abstract for some students, have them write the number strips to see how the formulas combine.

English Language Learners

Review the terms *vertex, vertices, edge,* and *face* before starting problem 17. English language learners may want to illustrate the terms on a pyramid and a prism when adding them to their vocabulary lists.

Hands-On Learning

Let students use plastic models of pyramids and prisms if these are available.

Solutions and Samples

15.

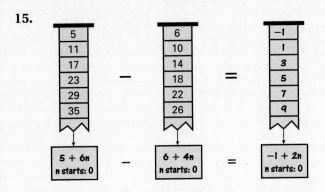

16. a. $(17 + 5n) + (13 - 7n) = 30 - 2n$

  b. $(17 + 5n) - (13 - 7n) = 4 + 12n$

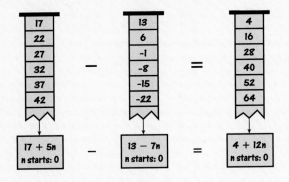

17. Answers will vary. Sample responses:
- the number of sides in the base
- the number of vertices in the base
- the number of faces, not counting the base

Hints and Comments

Overview

Students write expressions for two number sequences and for the sequence resulting from their subtraction. They also write expressions for the sum and for the difference of two more arithmetic sequences. Students investigate a sequence of pyramids.

Planning

Students may work on problem 15 individually. This problem may also be assigned as homework. They may work on problem 16 in small groups. Be sure to discuss students' answers to both problems.

Comments About the Solutions

15. In this problem, the expressions for all three strips are left out. You may want to challenge students to find the expression for the subtraction of the sequences without filling in the third strip.

16. This is the first time no number strips are given at all. Encourage students to solve this problem without the strips. This may be too abstract for some students, however, since the second expression given involves a decreasing sequence. If students are having difficulty, encourage them to focus on the increase or decrease of one sequence at a time: For the first sequence, the increase is five for every step, and for the second sequence the decrease is seven for every step. Therefore, when you add (or subtract) these two strips, you get $(+5) + (-7) = -2$ and $(+5) - (-7) = 12$.

Some students may prefer to use a stacked form:

$$\begin{array}{r} 17 + 5n \\ + \ 13 - 7n \\ \hline 30 - 2n \end{array}$$

$$\begin{array}{r} 17 + \ 5n \\ - \ 13 - \ 7n \\ \hline 4 + 12n \end{array}$$

17. There are several possible solutions. You may give students the hint to look at the numbers of faces, edges, and vertices (in each base as well as in each pyramid as a whole).

Extension

For problem 16 ask students for the first 3 terms in each sequence in the sequences of the sums and differences.

Notes

This number strip represents the number of vertices (V) for the sequence of pyramids. A **vertex** is the intersection of the edges of the pyramid.

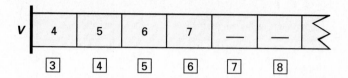

18. Find a formula for number strip V that relates V (the number of vertices) to n (the numbers below the pyramids). Where does n start?

19. a. Make number strips for the numbers of edges (E) and the numbers of faces (F) for the sequence of pyramids.

b. Write formulas for number strips E and F.

c. Combine number strips V, E, and F into a new number strip whose formula shows $V - E + F$.

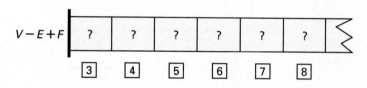

d. What's special about the number strip in part **c**? Explain this special property using the expressions for V, E, and F.

18 and 19 Monitor students as they make their strips and write the direct formulas. Be sure students write formulas that begin with $n = 3$, a change from the previous problems. Check that students have the correct formulas before they begin combining their strips in 19c.

19c Students are often quite surprised to get the same number each time and often think they have made a mistake when they get a strip of twos.

19d Students should show that adding and subtracting the formulas results in 2. Some students may need assistance with the algebra involved.

Assessment Pyramid

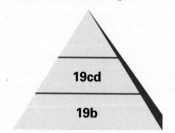

Write, combine, and generalize patterns related to Euler's formula.

Reaching All Learners

Accommodation

Some students may benefit from templates of the strips for V, E, F and $V - E + F$, using strips in the text as a model, for the pyramids and prisms.

Solutions and Samples

18. Expression for strip $V = n + 1$, n starts at 3.

19. a.

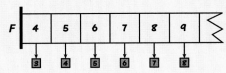

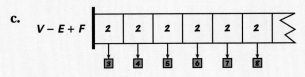

b. $E = 2n$ (n starts at 3)

$F = n + 1$ (n starts at 3)

c.

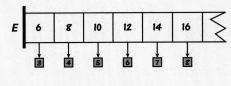

d. strip V: $n + 1$

strip E: $2n$

strip F: $n + 1$

$V - E + F$ results in: $(n + 1) - (2n) + (n + 1) =$

$n + 1 - 2n + n + 1 =$

$n + n - 2n + 2 =$

2

Hints and Comments

Overview

Students investigate a sequence of pyramids. They make number strips and write direct formulas for the numbers of vertices, faces, and edges in each consecutive pyramid. They combine the strips and formulas into a new strip with the expression $V - E + F$, and then describe the resulting special property.

About the Mathematics

The formula $V - E + F = 2$ is known as Euler's formula, which students studied in the unit *Packages and Polygons*. The formula is described on Student Book page 17.

Planning

Students may work on problems 18 and 19 in small groups. Be sure to discuss their answers before proceeding with subsequent problems. You may first want to review the terms vertices, edges, and faces.

Comments About the Solutions

19. c. You may want to check that students' number strips and expressions for V, E, and F (problems 18, 19a, and 19b) are correct before students begin making the combined strip.

Notes

Prisms

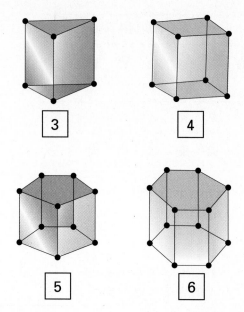

3 | 4

5 | 6

20. a. Make number strips *V, E,* and *F* for the sequence of prisms shown above.

b. Write expressions for number strips *V, E,* and *F* (expressed in terms of *n*).

c. Use the number strips or the expressions to check that $V - E + F = 2$ for prisms.

The formula $V - E + F = 2$ is called Euler's formula (Euler is pronounced "Oiler"). You have seen this formula in the *Packages and Polygons* unit. The formula works for many polyhedra. For example, an **icosahedron** has 20 faces. For any icosahedron, $V = 12$, $E = 30$, and $F = 20$. Using these values gives $12 - 30 + 20 = 2$.

20 This problem is similar to problem 19, in which students made number strips and wrote direct formulas for pyramids.

20c Discuss with students that expressions can only be added if they all have the same START number, in this case starts at three.

Reaching All Learners

Extension

You may have students check the given values for *V, E,* and *F* and investigate whether Euler's formula works for an icosahedron.

Some questions could be posed to students. Ask. *How many faces on this ball have six edges? How many have five edges?* (Note that students may use Euler's formula to find out. There are 12 pentagons and 20 hexagons.)

Solutions and Samples

20. a.

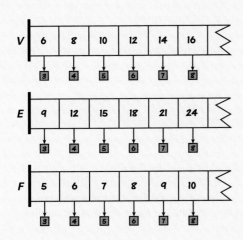

b. strip V: $2n$, n starts at 3.

strip E: $3n$, n starts at 3.

strip F: $n + 2$, n starts at 3.

c. $V - E + F$ results in: $(2n) - (3n) + (n + 2)$

$$= 2n - 3n + n + 2$$

$$= -n + n + 2$$

$$= 2$$

Hints and Comments

Overview

Students investigate a sequence of prisms. They make number strips and write direct formulas for V, E, and F, and by combining these they discover that Euler's formula works for prisms.

About the Mathematics

Make sure that students know what a polyhedron is: a solid formed by plane faces. Polyhedra are the subject of the unit *Packages and Polygons*.

Planning

Students may work on problem 20 individually. This problem may be assigned as homework. You may want to discuss students' answers as a class.

Comments About the Solutions

20. c. Students might also make the combination strip for $V - E + F$ to find that the values in the new strip are always 2.

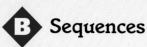

Notes

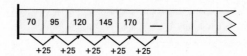
B Sequences

Summary

A sequence is called arithmetic if it has a constant increase or decrease at each step.

| 70 | 95 | 120 | 145 | 170 | — | | | |

+25 +25 +25 +25 +25

At *n* steps from the starting number 70, you get the number $70 + 25n$. This expression represents the sequence. Note that *n* starts at zero.

You can combine number sequences by adding or subtracting them. Adding or subtracting number sequences can be done using number strips or expressions.

For any polyhedron, Euler's formula $V - E + F = 2$ gives a relationship between the numbers of vertices, edges, and faces.

Many other sequences are not arithmetic, for instance the sequence formed by multiplying each term by $\frac{1}{2}$:

$$1, \frac{1}{2}, \frac{1}{4}, \frac{1}{8}.$$

A recursive formula for this sequence is NEXT = CURRENT $\times \frac{1}{2}$

Check Your Work

Belinda and Carmen are saving money from part-time jobs after school.

1. **a.** Belinda currently has $75. She decides to add $5 to her savings each week. Make a number strip that begins with 75 and shows Belinda's total savings every week. What are her savings after *n* weeks?

   b. Carmen currently has $125. Every week she adds twice as much as Belinda does. What are her savings after *n* weeks?

1 Some students may not recognize they are being asked for the direct formula or expression.

Assessment Pyramid

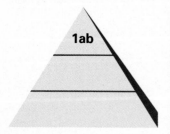

1ab

Assesses Section B Goals

Reaching All Learners

Parent Involvement

Have parents review the section with their child to relate the Check Your Work problems to the problems from the section.

Solutions and Samples

Answers to Check Your Work

1. a. After n weeks, Belinda has $75 + 5n$.

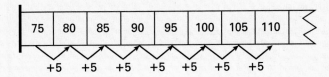

| 75 | 80 | 85 | 90 | 95 | 100 | 105 | 110 |

+5 +5 +5 +5 +5 +5 +5

b. $125 + 10n$. Strategies will vary. Sample student strategies:

- I can make an expression by seeing that 10 is double 5, and n still stands for the number of weeks.

- Students can make a strip first and then find the expression for that strip.

Hints and Comments

Overview

Students read and discuss the Summary. Then they use the Check Your Work problems as self-assessment. The answers to these problems are also provided in the Student Book.

Planning

After students finish Section B, you may assign as homework appropriate activities from the Additional Practice section, located on Student Book pages 40 and 41.

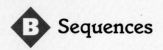
2b Look for a variety of strategies to share in class discussion.

Look again at the sequence.

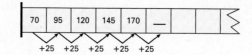

2. a. What is the 15th number in this sequence?

b. When does the value exceed 1,000 for the first time?

3. a. Make your own arithmetic sequence using fractions.

b. Write an expression that represents your sequence.

4. Reflect If you add two arithmetic sequences, do you always get an arithmetic sequence? Explain why or why not.

A five-sided tower is made by putting a five-sided pyramid on top of a five-sided prism, as shown below.

For this tower:

$V = 11$

$E = 20$

$F = 11$

5. a. Does Euler's formula work for a five-sided tower? Explain your answer.

b. Check to see whether Euler's formula works for an *n*-sided tower.

 For Further Reflection

Can you find a solid for which Euler's formula does not work? If you can, give an example.

Reaching All Learners

Intervention

For problem 5b, it may help some students to draw the towers for $n = 3$ and $n = 4$ to develop formulas for $V, E,$ and $F.$

Solutions and Samples

2. a. The 15th number is 420. The first number is 70, with $n = 0$. The 15th number will be $n = 14$, so $70 + 25 \times 14 = 420$.

b. The value exceeds 1,000 on the 39th number (when n is 38 or larger). Strategies will vary. Sample strategies:

- If the value of $70 + 25n$ must exceed 1,000, $25n$ must exceed 930. Therefore, n must be 38.

- $930 \div 25 = 37.2$, which can be rounded to 38.

- Multiply 25 by different numbers until the answer exceeds 930 (accounting for the additional 70).

   Continue to fill out the table until the answer exceeds 930.

3. a. Compare your sequence with that of a classmate. Let him or her check whether your expression fits. A sample arithmetic sequence using fractions is: 10, $7\frac{1}{2}$, 5, $2\frac{1}{2}$, 0, $-2\frac{1}{2}$, -5, $-7\frac{1}{2}$, etc.

   The constant *decrease* in this sample sequence is $2\frac{1}{2}$.

b. An expression that represents the sample sequence of 3a is $10 - 2\frac{1}{2}n$, n starts at zero.

4. Yes, when you add two arithmetic sequences together, you add the starting points, and you add the two changes. That means the new sequence will start at the sum of the two starts and will change by the sum of the two changes.

5. a. Yes. Euler's formula is $V - E + F = 2$; substituting the given values you get $11 - 20 + 11 = 2$.

b. Yes. For an n-sided tower,

$V = 2n + 1$

$E = 4n$

$F = 2n + 1$

$$V - E + F = (2n + 1) - 4n + (2n + 1)$$
$$= 2n + 2n - 4n + 2$$
$$= 2$$

For Further Reflection

A cylinder, cone, or sphere does not work. Those shapes do not have edges.

Hints and Comments

Overview

Students use the Check Your Work problems as self-assessment. The answers to these problems are also provided in the Student Book.

Planning

After students finish Section B, you may assign as homework appropriate activities from the Additional Practice section, located on Student Book pages 40 and 41.

Comments About the Solutions

5. Students may need help to see that there is a sharing of vertices, edges, and faces in the combination of pyramid and prism.

Section Focus

In this section, students investigate the sequence of square numbers by investigating number sequences, geometric patterns and an area model. Students generate the square numbers from a tile pattern and then represent the sequence in a number strip. They use square dot patterns to explain the increases in the number strip and use the pattern of increases to extend the sequence of square numbers. Students then use an area model to represent the square of a number and write related expressions. (Square numbers were also addressed in the unit *Facts and Factors*.)

Pacing and Planning

Day 8: Looking at Squares		Student pages 20–23
INTRODUCTION	Problems 1 and 2	Determine the dimensions of the largest square patio that can be made using 200 square tiles that measure 30 centimeters by 30 centimeters.
CLASSWORK	Problems 3–9	Investigate the step-by-step increase in the sequence of square numbers and use an area model to represent square numbers.
HOMEWORK	Problems 10 and 11	Extend a square-tile pattern and determine the new number of tiles.

Day 9: Shifted Strips		Student pages 23–25
INTRODUCTION	Review homework.	Review homework from Day 8.
CLASSWORK	Problems 12–17	Add the number strips for the odd and square number sequences and use an area model to investigate squaring the expression for the $(n + 1)$ sequence.
HOMEWORK	Problems 18 and 19	Write the number sequence and expanded expression for $(n + 4)^2$.

Day 10: Summary		Student pages 25–27
INTRODUCTION	Review homework.	Review homework from Day 9.
CLASSWORK	Additional Practice, pages 41 and 42	Create a direct formula from a tile pattern. Explain the connection between a visual pattern and a direct formula.
HOMEWORK	Check Your Work	Student self-assessment: Investigate the relationship between the sequence of square numbers and symbolic expressions.

Day 11: Summary		Student page 27
INTRODUCTION	Review homework.	Review homework from Day 10.
ASSESSMENT	Quiz 2	Assessment of Section A–C Goals
HOMEWORK	For Further Reflection	Investigate the validity of Euler's formula for other solids.

Additional Resources: *Algebra Tools*, Additional Practice, Section C, Student Book pages 41 and 42

Materials

Student Resources

No resources required

Teachers Resources

No resources required

Student Materials

No materials required

* See Hints and Comments for optional materials

Learning Lines

Number Sense

Students determine the dimensions of the largest square patio that can be made using 200 square tiles that measure 30 centimeters by 30 centimeters. Later they will determine how many squares they can make using the 200 tiles.

Patterns and Regularities

Students add number strips for the odd and square number sequences. They discover that the resulting sequence is the square number sequence without the zero term (shifted up by one) and can be represented by the expression $(n + 1)^2$. Next, students use an area model to investigate squaring the expression for the $(n + 1)$ sequence and add number strips to form the $(n + 2)^2$ sequence. Students then represent the $(n + 2)^2$ sequence with an area model. They then demonstrate their ability to describe the square number sequence and use an area model to square algebraic expressions. Students generalize a concrete number sequence to an expression that describes the sequence.

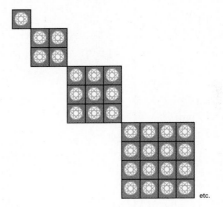

etc.

Models

Students use visual models to extend their understanding of equivalent expressions and formulas. For example:

- Students use square dot patterns to explain the increases in the number strip.

- Students use an area model to square numbers; for example, a number like 32 is broken into 30 and 2 and then used to label two sides of a square. The area model generates an expression with four terms—in this case: $(30 \times 30) + (30 \times 2) + (30 \times 2) + (2 \times 2) = 900 + 60 + 60 + 4 = 1024$

- Students use an area model to investigate squaring the expression $(n + 1)^2$.

At the End of this Section: Learning Outcomes

Students understand the sequence of square numbers. They justify equivalent expressions. They use visual models to extend their understanding of equivalent expressions and formulas. They create and use expressions and direct formulas to describe number sequences.

Notes

Some students will give the dimensions in terms of tiles. Remind them they know the dimensions of each tile.

To review metric measures, you might ask students to give the answer in meters as well as in centimeters.

Students should recognize that they need a number that when multiplied by itself is as close to 200 as possible. The square root of 200 is about 14.14.

Share strategies for finding the number of tiles needed. Some students should recognize that they can take the square root of 200 and round down, since they need whole tiles. Others may use a guess-and-check strategy.

Square Numbers

Looking at Squares

The Jacksons want to tile a square patio in their backyard. They bought 200 tiles; each tile measures 30 cm by 30 cm.

1. What are the dimensions of the largest square patio they can make?

After looking at several plans, they decide to arrange the tiles in a more imaginative way. The plan below shows four tiled squares.

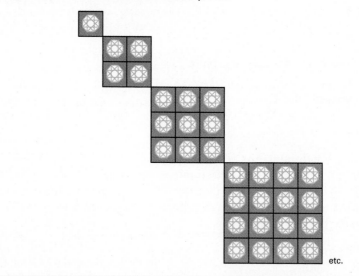

etc.

Reaching All Learners

Intervention

Ask students who have difficulty to give possible dimensions of a rectangle with an area of 200 tiles. Ask if any of these are squares and if they can make a square with 200 tiles. You might tell them they will not use all the tiles.

Solutions and Samples

1. 420 cm × 420 cm. The largest square patio that one can make with 200 tiles is one that is 14 tiles × 14 tiles, using a total of 196 tiles. If each tile is 30 cm × 30 cm, the patio would be 420 cm × 420 cm.

Hints and Comments

Overview

Students refresh their knowledge of squares by solving a problem about multiple squares. Square numbers are also addressed in the unit *Facts and Factors*.

Planning

You may want to work on problem 1 as a whole-class activity.

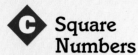
Notes

2 Students will need to keep a cumulative total so they know when they've used 200 tiles or will go over.

3 Discuss this question as a class. In particular, look for different ways students describe the increases shown in the sequence.

4 Monitor student responses. Share ideas if you have a variety. Students benefit from hearing other ways to visualize the patterns.

---

2. What is the largest square the Jacksons can make using this design with 200 tiles available?

To solve problem 2, you may have used the sequence of **square numbers**.

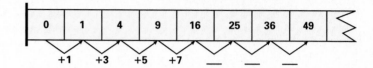

3. a. Why is 0 considered a square number?

   b. Describe the increases in the sequence of squares.

   c. Is this an arithmetic sequence? Why or why not?

The term "perfect square" becomes clear if you look at dot patterns. You can show 16 as a dot pattern with 4 rows of 4 dots.

4. Use the dot patterns below to describe the increase in the sequence of perfect square numbers.

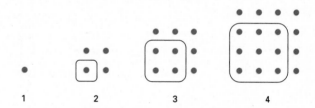

    1   2   3   4

Assessment Pyramid

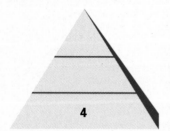

Relate verbal rule and diagram of nonarithmetic sequence.

Reaching All Learners

Accommodation

For problem 3, provide students who need assistance with a grid to help them organize their work, with headings such as these: tiled square number, drawing of this square, number of tiles in this square, total of tiles used in all squares so far (including this one).

Vocabulary Building

Some students are surprised to see there is a relationship between the term *square number* and the square shape! The dot pattern illustrates this nicely. Question 3c provides a good opportunity to review the meaning of the term *arithmetic sequence*.

Solutions and Samples

2. With 200 tiles, the largest square the Jacksons can make has sides of 14 squares and consists of 196 tiles.

Students might also reason that the problem includes all squares in the set. That is, 1-by-1, 2-by-2, 3-by-3, and so on. In this case, the solution would be the set of squares up to 7-by-7. The total number of squares would be $1 + 4 + 9 + 16 + 25 + 36 + 49 = 140$.

To add the 8-by-8 square to the set, the Jacksons would need 64 more tiles.

3. a. Zero is a square number because it is equal to 0^2, $0 \times 0 = 0$.

b. The sequence of increases is the sequence of odd numbers.

c. The sequence is *not* arithmetic since there is no constant increase or decrease.

4. The increases are the sequence of odd numbers. For each new square, the increase is two more than the previous increase, as shown below.

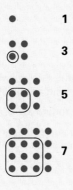

Hints and Comments

Overview

Students explore square patterns, square numbers, and how the sequence of square numbers increases. Students use the dot patterns to describe the increase in the sequence of square numbers

About the Mathematics

In previous sections, students investigated linear or arithmetic number sequences. In this section, the sequence of square numbers is studied. The sequence of differences between consecutive square numbers is linear.

In mathematical terms, the study of differences is known as "differential calculus." Although formal calculus is not used in this or other units in *Mathematics in Context*, the problems in this section establish the conceptual foundation of rates of change studied later in calculus.

In the unit *Ups and Downs*, students also study differences and make use of a "difference diagram" to visualize the linearity of the differences. In *Building Formulas*, squares and square roots are formally introduced.

In general, to move from one square number, n^2, to the next square number, $(n + 1)^2$, add $2n + 1$; $(n + 1)^2 = n^2 + 2n + 1$.

Planning

You may want students to work on problems 2, 3, and 4 in small groups. For some students, you may need to review perfect square numbers.

Comments About the Solutions

2. Some students will know what the square numbers are; others will need to take a more concrete approach and draw the subsequent square patterns.

4. See the comment in the About the Mathematics section on the next page concerning V-numbers. Each next square number (dot pattern) can be made from the previous square number by adding a V-number.

Extension

You may want to challenge some students to relate the expression for the odd numbers ($2n + 1$) to the increase shown in the dot patterns for square numbers.

Square Numbers

Notes

5 Students need to apply what they have learned about the increase between square numbers.

7 Ask students to estimate the square of 32 before beginning problem 7. Share estimates and strategies for estimating, as well as which might be the best estimates and why.

7 Discuss this problem as a class. Be sure students understand partitioning the numbers and the relationship between the products and area. It is important to understand the model using numbers before using it for algebraic expressions.

8 Be sure students use the area models and don't just use their calculators!

The squares of 20 and 21 are 400 and 441, respectively. This can be written as $20^2 = 400$ and $21^2 = 441$.

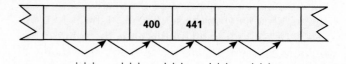

5. a. Without multiplying, find the square of 22.

  b. Do the same for the square of 18.

The sequence of square numbers forms several patterns.

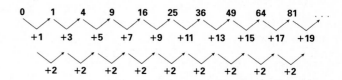

6. a. Describe the patterns of the sequence of the square numbers in your own words.

  b. Continue the sequence of squares for six more numbers.

Area Drawings

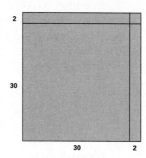

Another way to find the square of a number is by using a diagram such as this one.

7. Explain how to find 32^2 using the diagram.

8. a. Make a drawing like the one shown here to help you calculate 43^2.

  b. Do the same for 57^2.

Assessment Pyramid

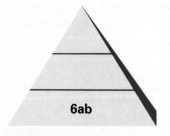

Summarize and apply patterns in the sequence of square numbers.

Reaching All Learners

Intervention

If students have difficulty with problem 5, ask them to copy the strip and write the increases underneath. From 400 to 441, the increase is 41. What is the next increase? Some students will have more difficulty working backward to find 18^2 than adding on to find 22^2.

Extension

You may want to give students a series of numbers and have them explain (using dot patterns) why the numbers are square or not. Have them show with dot patterns what the next and the previous square numbers will be. Possible numbers are 24, 64, 50, and 110.

Solutions and Samples

5. a. The square of 22 is 484. Students should note that since the increases are the odd numbers and the previous step increased by 41, the next increase must be 43. So the square of 22 is $441 + 43 = 484$.

   b. The square of 18 is 324. Students can work backward.
   $400 - 39 = 361$ (19^2)
   $361 - 37 = 324$ (18^2)

6. a. Descriptions will vary. Sample description: The numbers in the top row (the square numbers) increase by the sequence of odd numbers. In the second row, each increase is always two more than the previous one.

   b.

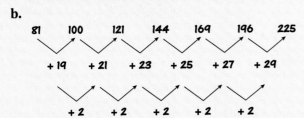

7. Dividing the area into four sections results in four regions where the areas can be found by multiplication.

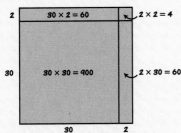

$900 + 60 + 60 + 4 = 1{,}024$; so $32^2 = 1{,}024$.

8. a.

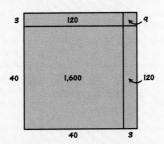

$1{,}600 + 120 + 120 + 9 = 1{,}849$; so $43^2 = 1{,}849$.

   b.

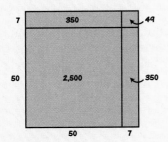

$2{,}500 + 350 + 350 + 49 = 3{,}249$; so $57^2 = 3{,}249$.

Hints and Comments

Overview

Students investigate the increases in the sequence of squares and use this information to find square numbers in a series. Students use an area model to extend their knowledge of square numbers.

About the Mathematics

In general, to move from one square number, n^2, to the next square number, $(n+1)^2$, add $2n + 1$; $(n + 1)^2 = n^2 + 2n + 1$.

Applying this rule, to move from the square of 20 to the square of 21, one adds 41. This is the 21st odd number or, in other words, the V-number for $n = 20$, since 3 is the first V-number and the second odd number.

Any square number can be pictured with a square diagram representing the area. Students may partition the area models of the squares in a variety of ways.

Knowing the squares of easy numbers, such as $10^2 = 100$, $20^2 = 400$, and $15^2 = 225$, can be helpful in finding the squares of more difficult numbers.

Planning

After students complete problem 6, you may want to have a thorough class discussion about problems 2–6. In this discussion, make sure students understand what a square number is and that the differences between square numbers form the sequence of odd numbers.

Comments About the Solutions

5. Students need not write down this rule in any formal way. It is sufficient if they understand that the increase is an odd number, and that in each next step, the increase is by the next odd number.

7. If students are having difficulty, you may want to ask them what the area of the diagram is.

8. Problem 8 is critical because it is the first time students are asked to construct an area model to find the square of a number. You may want to give students time to explore this problem and discuss it among themselves.

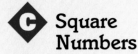

Square Numbers

Notes

9 This problem deals with a common misconception. Ask students who think the calculation is correct to make an area model to show how this works.

10 You may want to ask students to estimate the product first. This helps students identify, and hopefully correct, the common misconception that $(2\frac{1}{2})^2 = 4\frac{1}{4}$.

11 If students are confused, ask them how many tiles are on each edge of the original square. Drawing a diagram to show where the new tiles are added may also be helpful.

Donald wrote down these calculations:

$$
\begin{array}{r}
200^2 = 40,000 \\
+ \quad 1^2 = \quad\quad 1 \\
\hline
201^2 = 40,001
\end{array}
$$

9. Do you agree with the calculations above? Explain why or why not.

10. Use the area diagram to show that $(2\frac{1}{2})^2 = 6\frac{1}{4}$.

11. Jackie has a square patio made of 1,444 square tiles. She wants to extend two sides of the patio as shown below. How many extra tiles does she need?

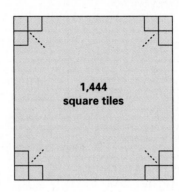

1,444 square tiles

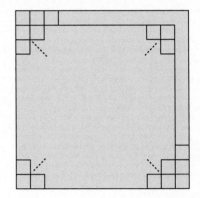

Shifted Strips

The square of a number n can be written as $n \cdot n$ or as n^2. The next number after n can be written as $n + 1$, so the square of $n + 1$ is $(n + 1) \cdot (n + 1)$ or $(n + 1)^2$.

12. How can you write the next number after $n + 1$? How can you write the square of that number?

Assessment Pyramid

11

Apply pattern of square numbers.

Reaching All Learners

Intervention

Model problem 11 with smaller squares, using tiles. The total number of tiles in the starting square can be modified to a smaller square number for some students, if needed.

For students who have trouble with the abstract notation in problem 12, ask them to count from several different start numbers and explain how they know what comes next. Then ask them to start with n and explain how we can count from there.

Solutions and Samples

9. No. Donald forgot that if you draw a picture of 201, there are four parts to it. He forgot the parts showing 200×1 and 1×200. So his answer is 400 less than the correct answer 40,401.

10.

If you add up all of the parts: $4 + 1 + 1 + \frac{1}{4} = 6\frac{1}{4}$.

11. Jackie needs 77 extra tiles. The total of 1,444 tiles is 38×38, so there are 38 tiles on each side of the original patio. She would need to add $38 + 38 + 1$, or 77 tiles.

12. The next number is $n + 2$. Its square is $(n + 2) \times (n + 2)$, or $(n + 2)^2$.

Hints and Comments

Overview

Students use an area model to extend their knowledge of square numbers.

About the Mathematics

Any square number can be pictured with a square diagram representing the area. It is important to understand the area model since it makes very clear that, for example, 201^2 is not the same as 200^2 plus 1^2. Adding squares to get the new square is a common mistake, and the area model is intended to prevent students from making this mistake. Students may partition the area models of the squares in a variety of ways.

Planning

You may have students work on problems 9 and 10 in small groups and problem 11 individually.

Comments About the Solutions

10. In this problem, students need to show an understanding of what squaring means.

C Square Numbers

Notes

13b You might ask students why this section is titled "Shifted Strips." This helps students think about how the strips of square numbers are shifted to a new position in the list of square numbers.

14 Students need to recognize the sequence begins with $n = 0$.

14 and 15 Be sure students understand how each expression describes the sequence of square numbers. Students can verify that each formula works by testing different values of n. It is important for students to understand that if two formulas correctly describe the same sequence, then hose formulas must be equivalent.

16 It is important for students to recognize how the area diagram represents the multiplication problem.

Larry (the boy who was investigating the odd numbers) decides to add his sequence of odd numbers to the n^2 sequence (where n starts at 0).

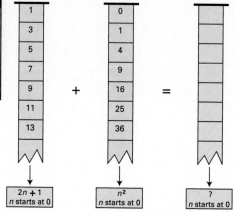

13. Copy the three number strips above into your notebook.
    a. Find the missing numbers and the expression for the third strip.
    b. What do you notice about the number sequence in the third strip?

14. Larry wrote the expression $(n + 1)^2$ for the third strip. Is he correct? Explain why or why not.

15. If you add the expressions of the first and second number strip, what is the answer?

Larry says, "I have two expressions for the same number strip: $(n + 1)^2$ and $n^2 + 2n + 1$. The two expressions must be equivalent."

16. Copy and use the diagram to explain Larry's statement, $(n + 1)^2 = n^2 + 2n + 1$, in a different way.

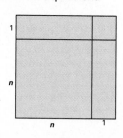

Assessment Pyramid

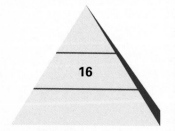

16

Justify equivalent expressions.

Reaching All Learners

Intervention

For problem 16, some students may need to talk through finding the area of each section using algebraic notation. Watch for students who confuse n^2 with $2n$ and $1n$ with $1 + n$.

Vocabulary Building

Review the meaning of the term *equivalent*. What two root words can you find in this term? (equal, value)

Solutions and Samples

13. a.

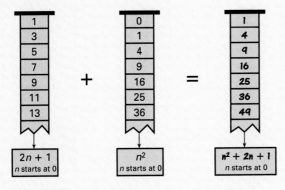

b. It is the n^2 sequence starting at 1 instead of 0.

14. Yes. Explanations will vary. One way to show that $(n + 1)^2$ fits the numbers on the third strip is to let $n = 0, 1, 2, \ldots$ in the formula and check that they match the numbers on the third strip. Other students may notice that the third strip is the second strip shifted up one. If the second strip is represented by n^2, the shifted strip must be represented by $(n + 1)^2$, which is the second strip started one later.

15. $2n + 1 + n^2 = n^2 + 2n + 1$ and also: $2n + 1 + n^2 = (n + 1)^2$, which was Larry's answer.

16. Explanations will vary. Sample explanation:

The drawing can be seen to have an area of $(n + 1)^2$ because each side is length $n + 1$, so the total area is $(n + 1)^2$ or $(n + 1) \times (n + 1)$. The drawing can also be seen to have an area of $n^2 + 2n + 1$, because the four parts of the diagram have areas n^2, n, n, and 1.

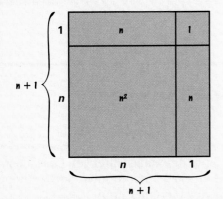

Hints and Comments

Overview

Number strips are used to describe the sequences of square numbers and of odd numbers. Students generalize the area model to visualize the increase from one square number to the next.

About the Mathematics

The area model used on the previous page is one way to visualize how to add the expressions $2n + 1$ and n^2. Number strips are another way. The area model is a geometric approach, and the number strips are a numerical approach. On this page, the sequence of square numbers is generalized by describing it with an expression.

It is important when adding expressions for number strips that the expressions start at the same n value. If one expression starts at $n = 0$ and another at $n = 1$, the sum of the expressions will not match the sum of the number strips.

In problem 14, a numerical approach is used to show that $2n + 1 + n^2 = (n + 1)^2$. In problem 16, a geometrical approach is used to show the same relationship.

Planning

You may have students work on problems 13–15 in small groups or pairs. Students may work on problem 16 individually. Students may need to copy the diagram so that they can use it to explain their reasoning.

Comments About the Solutions

13. Strategies will vary. Sample strategies:

- Add the numbers row by row and then find the direct expression by adding the expressions for the given sequences.

- Find the direct expression first and then find the numbers in the third number strip from the direct expression for the third strip.

- Fill in the numbers in the last strip and then look for a direct expression that describes this sequence.

14. It is not hard to see that the sequence in the last row is that of square numbers. Finding the correct expression is more difficult.

Extension

You may want students to explain how the area model and the number strip model on the previous page relate to each other.

Square Numbers

Notes

18 Before beginning this problem, have students identify as many patterns as they can in the information shown in the sequences and their formulas. Share these as a class. You might also want students to show the area models for these, too. The predictions should follow easily from this. Students should not be asked to memorize the formula for squaring a binomial, but should understand how to do this multiplication.

19 If students are stuck, ask what methods might work. Hopefully students will realize the area method should work here (as do others). Share and compare student strategies. Ask students how they can be sure their strategy is correct.

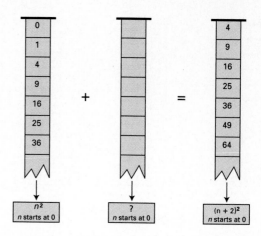

The $(n + 1)^2$ sequence starts one step later than the n^2 sequence. Larry wonders how to get a sequence that starts two steps later.

17. a. Copy and complete the number strip in the middle. Assume that n starts at 0 for each strip.

   b. What expression describes the second strip? (Be sure n starts at 0 with your expression.)

   c. Use the expressions from the first two strips to write an equivalent expression for $(n + 2)^2$.

   d. Use an area diagram to explain your answer in part **c**.

You can keep starting the sequence later by adding one more to n each time, as shown below.

Sequence	Formula, where n starts at 0 in each case
0, 1, 4, 9, 16,	$n^2 = n^2$
1, 4, 9, 16,	$(n + 1)^2 = n^2 + 2n + 1$
4, 9, 16,	$(n + 2)^2 = n^2 + 4n + 4$
9, 16,	$(n + 3)^2 = n^2 + 6n + 9$

18. By looking at patterns, predict what the equivalent expression for $(n + 4)^2$ would be. Where does the sequence start?

19. Find an equivalent expression for $(2n + 1)^2$. Explain your method and how you know it is correct.

Assessment Pyramid

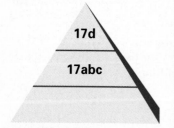

17d

17abc

Use visual models.

Combine number sequences and the corresponding expressions for squaring binomials.

Reaching All Learners

Advanced Learners

Challenge advanced learners who are comfortable with algebraic notation to use the area model to multiply other binomials. After you pose a few problems, they can write problems for each other to solve. Some students may generalize patterns for multiplying binomials from these experiences.

Solutions and Samples

17. a.

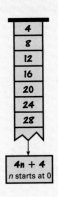

b. $4n + 4$

c. The expression is $n^2 + 4n + 4 = (n + 2)^2$.

d.

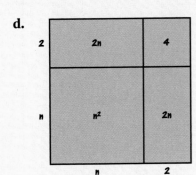

18. $n^2 + 8n + 16$, where n starts at 0 and the sequence starts at 16

19. $(2n + 1)^2 = 4n^2 + 4n + 1$

Strategies will vary. The expression can be found by using an area diagram or by looking at patterns.

Hints and Comments

Overview

Students use number strips to explore and investigate the relationship between number sequences and their corresponding expressions.

About the Mathematics

The strategies described for problem 14 may be applied here as well.

Planning

Students may work on problems 17 and 18 individually. After problem 17, you may want to have a brief class discussion about the number strips and the area model. Another option is to have students work on Problems 17 and 18 and then discuss these problems after students read the section Summary on the following page.

Comments About the Solutions

17. and 18.
It is important that students notice that the third strip is the first strip minus the first two entries.

18. You may want to suggest that students use a diagram to explain how the formulas are related to each other. The formula can be divided into three parts:

- The first part is n^2, and this is the same in each formula.

- The second part is a multiple of $2n$, and each next formula has $2n$ more.

- The third part is a square number, and each next formula has the next square number.

Notes

Students read and discuss the Summary reviewing how number sequences can be represented. Then they use the Check Your Work problems as self-assessment. The answers to these problems are also provided in the Student Book.

During the summary discussion, you may want to use the sequence $(n + 3)^2$ as an example and illustrate this sequence with the models used in this section. You may want to discuss problems 17 and 18 after the Summary discussion.

 Square Numbers

Summary

The square of a number is the number multiplied by itself. For example:

- The square of 4 is $4 \times 4 = 4^2 = 16$.
- The square of $3\frac{1}{2}$ is $3\frac{1}{2} \times 3\frac{1}{2} = (3\frac{1}{2})^2 = 12\frac{1}{4}$.
- The square of n is $n \cdot n = n^2$.

Numbers like 4, 9, $12\frac{1}{4}$, 36, 10,000 are called square numbers, and numbers like 4, 9, 36, 10,000 are perfect squares.

The same number strip can represent equivalent expressions.

$(n + 1)^2$ and $n^2 + 2n + 1$ are both represented by 1, 4, 9, 16, 25, ..., where n starts at zero.

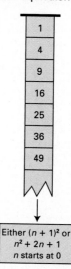

Either $(n + 1)^2$ or $n^2 + 2n + 1$
n starts at 0

An area diagram can also be used to show that $(n + 1)^2 = n^2 + 2n + 1$.

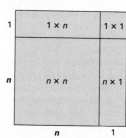

Reaching All Learners

Vocabulary Building

You may want to point out the difference between square numbers and perfect square numbers, like 4, 9, 16, 121, 196... (no fractions).

Hints and Comments

Overview

Students read and discuss the Summary, which reviews dot patterns and number strips. Then they use the Check Your Work problems as self-assessment. The answers to these problems are also provided in the Student Book.

About the Mathematics

Three models that may be used to visualize the sequence of square numbers are number strips, dot patterns, and area diagrams. The differences in a sequence provide information about the type of sequence it is. When the differences form an arithmetic sequence or linear relationship, the original sequence is quadratic (involving squares).

Planning

After students finish Section C, you may assign as homework appropriate activities from the Additional Practice section, located on Student Book pages 41 and 42.

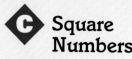

Square Numbers

Notes

2 There is only one perfect square in this interval. Ask students if they can find another number that is equal to a number times itself. If necessary, give the hint to try a fraction or decimal.

4 Students may use the area model to multiply or may apply the pattern they observed in problem 18.

5 If students have difficulty, ask them to describe the increase between terms. Can they continue this pattern? Some students may also see and apply a formula for the sequence. Share different strategies as a class.

Check Your Work

1. What is the largest square patio you can make with 68 square tiles? You may use only whole tiles.

2. Write down two square numbers between 30 and 40.

If you start the n^2 sequence three steps later, you get the $(n + 3)^2$ sequence.

3. Show that $(n + 3)^2$ is the same as the expression $n^2 + 6n + 9$ by using an area diagram.

4. Write an expression that is equivalent to $(n + 10)^2$.

Here is a sequence of squares that can be extended as far as you wish.

0	4	16	36	64	100	144	....

5. Use regularities in the pattern to find the next three numbers of the sequence. (Hint: Look again at problem 6.)

For Further Reflection

Sully says that the square of a number is the same as the number times two. Is he ever right? Explain why or why not.

Assessment Pyramid

3, 5

1, 2, 4, ☐FFR

Assesses Section C Goals

Reaching All Learners

Advanced Learners

Challenge advanced learners to write a direct formula for the sequence shown in problem 5.

Extension

Have students use the area model and number strips to explain the equivalent expressions.

Solutions and Samples

Answers to Check Your Work

1. A square patio of $8 \times 8 = 64$ tiles, so 4 tiles are left. If you answered a square patio of 17 tiles in length and width, you only placed your squares at the perimeter of the patio and the patio itself is filled with sand.

2. 36 is a square number because $6 \times 6 = 36$. It is the only perfect square between 30 and 40.

   $30\frac{1}{4}$ is a square number because $5\frac{1}{2} \times 5\frac{1}{2} = 30\frac{1}{4}$.

   Note that square numbers do not have to be whole numbers!

3.

3	3n	9
n	n^2	3n
	n	3

4. $n^2 + 20n + 100$. You can find this expression by looking at number strips, by drawing an area diagram as shown below, or possibly by doing symbol manipulation.

10	10n	100
n	n^2	10n
	n	10

5. The next three numbers of the sequence are 196, 256, and 324. Look at the regularities in the sequence shown below.

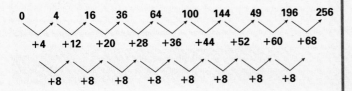

0   4   16   36   64   100   144   49   196   256

+4   +12   +20   +28   +36   +44   +52   +60   +68

+8   +8   +8   +8   +8   +8   +8   +8

For Further Reflection

There is only one case when Sully's statement is true, for the number 2. That is, 2 squared is the same as 2 times 2.

Hints and Comments

Overview

Students read and discuss the Summary, which reviews dot patterns and number strips. Then they use the Check Your Work problems as self-assessment. The answers to these problems are also provided in the Student Book.

Section Focus

Students apply the square number sequence to solve problems involving a tessellated triangle pattern. Students name basic polygons and investigate a sequence of tessellated equilateral triangles. They discover that the total number of triangles in the pattern can be represented by the square number sequence. Students then rearrange the white and red triangles in the pattern to show that the number of tiles in the tessellation is equal to the square of the number tiles in the base.

Pacing and Planning

Day 12: Tessellations and Tiles		Student pages 28–31
INTRODUCTION	Problems 1–4	Name basic polygons and investigate a sequence of tessellated equilateral triangles.
CLASSWORK	Problem 6	Rearrange the white and red triangles to show that the number of tiles in the tessellation is equal to the square of the number of tiles in the base.
HOMEWORK	Problems 5 and 7	Determine the number of white and colored triangles that cover a rectangular and triangular surface.

Day 13: Triangular Numbers		Student pages 32 and 33
INTRODUCTION	Problem 8	Investigate the connections between triangle tessellations, dot patterns, and triangular numbers.
CLASSWORK	Problems 9–12	Investigate the rectangular numbers and analyze formulas for rectangular and triangular numbers.
HOMEWORK	Problem 13	Evaluate the formula for the triangular numbers.

Day 14: The Ping-Pong Competition		Student pages 34 and 35
INTRODUCTION	Problem 16	Extend a table that lists the number of ping-pong matches played.
CLASSWORK	Problems 17–20	Analyze patterns in the table and write a direct formula.
HOMEWORK	Problems 14 and 15	Apply the formula for triangular numbers.

Day 15: Summary		Student pages 34 and 36–38
INTRODUCTION	Review homework.	Review homework from Day 14.
ASSESSMENT	Check Your Work For Further Reflection	Student self-assessment: Describe and analyze various dot patterns and problem contexts with algebraic expressions.
UNIT REVIEW	Summary Sections	Review the main topics of the unit as outlined in Section Summaries A–D.

Additional Resources: *Algebra Tools*, Additional Practice, Section D, Student Book pages 42 and 43

Materials

Student Resources

Quantities listed are per student.

• **Student Activity Sheets 2** and **3**

Teachers Resources

No resources required

Student Materials

No materials required

* See Hints and Comments for optional materials

Learning Lines

Patterns and Regularities

Students investigate the connections between triangle tessellations, dot patterns, and triangular numbers. Then using the dot pattern for the rectangular numbers, students justify two different formulas for the rectangular numbers and demonstrate that each rectangular number is double a triangular number. Students write a formula for the triangular numbers and apply this formula to solve problems involving a stack of cans.

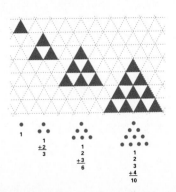

Students extend a table that lists the number of ping-pong matches played at a competition with various numbers of players. After listing the number sequence and drawing a diagram to represent the context, students write a direct formula that they can use to calculate the number of ping-pong matches played in the competition with any number of players.

Number of Players	Graph	Number of Games
2		1
3		3
4		6

At the End of this Section: Learning Outcomes

Students use triangular and rectangular numbers as examples of describing sequences. They also use formulas and expressions to describe patterns and sequences in realistic situations.

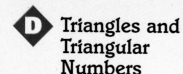

Triangles and Triangular Numbers

Notes

Triangles and Triangular Numbers

Tessellations and Tiles

Here is a collection of tiles. You may have seen these shapes before in the *Packages and Polygons* unit.

1. Name the shape of each tile above.

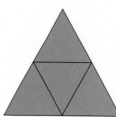

In the *It's All the Same* unit, you saw that you can tessellate or cover the plane using any triangle. With a triangular tile, you can also tessellate a triangle that is exactly the same shape as the basic tile. On the left, an equilateral triangle tessellates a larger equilateral triangle.

If you alternate purple and white tiles, you can create triangles with interesting patterns.

      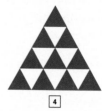

1   2   3   4

2. **a.** Find the total number of tiles used for each of the triangles.

b. How many tiles do you need to add a row to the base of the fourth triangle to get the fifth pattern?

2 You may want to discuss patterns students can find in this sequence of triangles as an introduction to the problem.

Reaching All Learners

Accommodation

You may want to make a transparency of these shapes and do this problem as a whole-class activity. You might cut out and color the shapes to see which of them tessellate.

Vocabulary Building

The introduction provides an opportunity to review the meaning of the term *polygon* and the names of some basic shapes. A term most students will need to review is *rhombus*. Have students write a definition of the term *polygon* and the names of the shapes, together with an illustration of each in their notebooks.

Solutions and Samples

1.

 square

 triangle

 hexagon

 quadrilateral, rhombus, parallelogram, or diamond

 pentagon

2. a.

Triangle Number	1	2	3	4	5
Total Tiles	1	4	9	16	25

   b. You need nine more tiles to make the fifth triangle: five purple and four white. (See the table above.)

Hints and Comments

Materials

transparency of the shapes shown on page 28 of the Student Book, optional (one per class);

Overview

Students identify different shapes of tiles. They use the names of the shapes that they learned in the unit *Packages and Polygons*. Students determine the number of small purple and white triangular tiles needed to create larger triangles.

About the Mathematics

Students discover that the total number of tiles in a triangular tessellation is equal to the number of tiles in the base of the tessellation squared. The triangular tile pattern is another way to visualize square numbers.

Planning

You may want to briefly review the term *tessellation* before students begin working on the problems on this page. Students may work on problems 1 and 2 in small groups.

Note: When a problem in this section refers to tiles, it means white and colored tiles together. Otherwise, it will specify white or colored tiles.

Comments About the Solutions

2. You may want to suggest to students that they count the number of tiles and list the results in a table. This will help them recognize that the total number of tiles is the square of the number of purple tiles in the base.

D Triangles and Triangular Numbers

Notes

4 Most students will see this pattern as n^2, with the values of n starting at 1. Some students may connect this with the shifted strips and write $(n + 1)^2$, with n starting at 0.

5a If students have not already connected the number of rows to the number of triangles in the bottom row, have them return to the pictures of the first four terms in the pattern to look for this relationship.

5b Students can see the bottom row, so they can use this to determine the pattern number and the total number of triangles.

3. Find the total number of tiles needed to make the tenth triangle in the sequence.

The number of tiles in each triangle in the sequence is shown on the number strip.

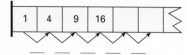

4. **a.** What is the 30th number in this sequence?

   b. Use n to write an expression for this number strip. Where does n start?

Janet is building a triangle table. She wants to completely cover the table with triangle tiles. A newspaper is covering most of the table so that only one row of triangles can be seen.

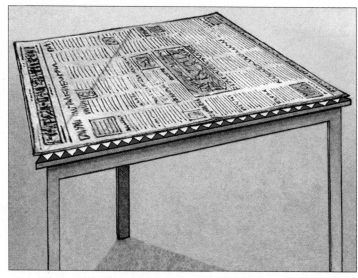

5. **a.** How many rows of triangles cover the table?

   b. Find the total number of tiles that are hidden by the newspaper.

Assessment Pyramid

4ab, 5ab

Apply patterns of triangular numbers.

Reaching All Learners

Accommodation

For problem 5. you may cut out and color the shapes to see which of them tessellate. You may want to provide students with a chart to fill in; headings can include pattern number, number of rows, number of blue triangles in the bottom row, total number of blue triangles, number of white triangles, and total number of triangles (both colors).

Writing Opportunity

Problem 5 can be used as a writing opportunity. You can ask students to write one or two paragraphs in which they describe the reasoning they used to solve this problem.

Solutions and Samples

3. 100 tiles. Strategies will vary. Students might notice that the table shows that the total number of tiles is the square of the triangle number. For triangle number 10, 100 tiles are needed.

4. a. $30^2 = 900$

   b. n^2; n starts at 1.

5. a. There are 27 rows since you can count 27 blue tiles in the last row.

   b. 676. Strategies will vary. Sample strategies:

   Twenty-six rows are hidden. This means that there are 26^2 or 676 tiles hidden by the newspaper.

   Alternately, there are a total of $27^2 = 729$ tiles, so that there are $729 - 27 - 26 = 676$ tiles. Since there are 27 blue tiles showing and 26 white tiles showing, the number of hidden tiles is 676 ($729 - 27 - 26 = 676$).

Hints and Comments

Overview

The number strip is revisited as a model to describe the number of tiles in a tessellation of a triangle. Students extend the triangular pattern to a larger tessellation.

About the Mathematics

On this page, the connection with the sequence of square numbers is made explicit through the number strip.

Planning

Students may work on problems 3 and 4 in small groups. They may work on problem 5 individually. Problem 5 can be assigned as homework.

Comments About the Solutions

3. It may be necessary for some students to draw the triangle and count to find the pattern. Other students may see the pattern after a couple of rows.

4. This problem is critical because students use the expression n^2 for the sequence of perfect squares. They should recognize that the 30th number is the square of 30. Encourage students to make a connection with what they have done in the previous sections.

5. This problem can be assigned as homework. Remind students to look at both the white and the blue tiles.

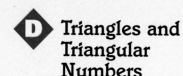
Activity

Triangular Patterns

As you found on the previous page, you can use a simple rule to calculate the number of tiles in a triangular **tessellation**. If there are n tiles along the base of the tessellation, then the total number of tiles is equal to n^2.

Study the triangular tessellations to see one explanation of why the rule stated above works.

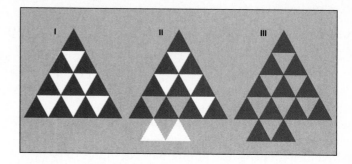

6 This problem allows students to verify that the total number of triangles is n^2 using a visual reasoning.

Use **Student Activity Sheet 2** to answer problem 6.

6. a. Starting with Figure I, reflect every white triangle over the base of the triangle (Figure II). Color each reflected triangle red (Figure III).

b. Explain why the total number of tiles in Figure I is equal to the number of red tiles in the finished version of Figure III.

c. The rule states that the total number of tiles in Figure I is equal to 4^2. Explain this using the finished version of Figure III.

d. Verify the rule for a triangle with five rows ($n = 5$).

6d Triangle grid paper may help students draw the diagram to verify the rule for $n = 5$. A sheet of this grid paper can be divided in fourths.

Reaching All Learners

Accommodation

Draw the triangle diagram on triangular grid paper and copy for students to assist in drawing the flipped triangles. Alternatively, give students who have difficulty some tracing paper or small piece of a transparency. Have them trace the white triangles and color them dark. Flip the paper or transparency so the dark triangles are in position and tape down.

Vocabulary Building

Have students offer their explanation for what *tessellation* is. Some students might recall this term from the unit *Reallotment*.

Solutions and Samples

6. a.

There are six reflected triangles.

b. Explanations will vary, but students should note that none of the triangles disappeared, some were merely moved and colored red. The number of red triangles added is equal to the number of white triangles. The other red triangles have not moved. So the finished version of Figure III represents all the triangles.

c. Sample explanation:

The rule says that the total number of triangles is 4^2 (because 4 is the number of triangles in the base). If you turn the last diagram on its side, it is a parallelogram (rhombus). There are four rows of four triangles, to make a total of 16 triangles.

d. Reflecting the white tiles in a triangle with five rows results in a rhombus that is made up of five rows of five tiles. There is a total of 5×5, or 25 tiles.

Hints and Comments

Materials

Student Activity Sheet 2 (one per student); tracing paper, optional (one sheet per student); black markers, optional (one per student)

Overview

Students explore a strategy that explains why the total number of tiles in a tessellation of a triangle is equal to the square of the number of tiles in the base. Then they solve a problem in which they apply this strategy.

About the Mathematics

The rule for finding the total number of tiles in a triangular tessellation is made explicit. This rule is true for triangles that are made up of similar smaller triangles.

Planning

You may want to have students work on problem 6 individually.

Comments About the Solutions

6. This is an example of a visual proof and should help students to think "visually." Visual reasoning and visual proofs are very important because students will become more confident about their mathematical knowledge if they can visualize processes.

Triangles and Triangular Numbers

Notes

7 Look for a variety of strategies. Share strategies in whole class discussion.

7. a. Determine how many white triangles are in the tessellation above without counting each one. Explain your method.

b. How many red triangles are there?

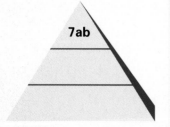
Reaching All Learners

Accommodation

For students who are overwhelmed with this problem, reduce the size of the figure to five rows, and then ten rows, by covering up the rest of the triangles.

Solutions and Samples

7. a. There are 66 white triangles. Sample strategies:

Row	White Triangles
1	11
2	10
3	9
4	8
5	7
6	6
7	5
8	4
9	3
10	2
11	1
TOTAL:	**66**

Students may count the white triangles in a few of the rows to establish a pattern and then use that pattern to fill in the numbers for the other rows.

Another way of finding the sum is to pair up numbers: add the white triangles in the first and last rows, then the white triangles in the second and next-to-last rows, and so on: $(1 + 11) + (2 + 10) + (3 + 9) + (4 + 8) + (5 + 7) + 6 = 5 \times 12 + 6 = 66$ white triangles

b. There are 78 red triangles. Sample strategies: There are 12 rows, and in each row there is one more red than white triangle, $66 + 12 = 78$.

The total number of tiles (T) is 144 (or 12^2).

The total number of red tiles (B) must be equal to the total number of tiles (T) minus the total number of white tiles (W). This can be represented by $B = T - W$. So $B = 144 - 66 = 78$.

Hints and Comments

Overview

Students solve a problem in which they have to find the number of white and red triangles in a large tessellation.

Planning

Students may work individually on problem 7.

Comments About the Solutions

7. Several steps are needed to solve this problem.

D Triangles and Triangular Numbers

Notes

Triangular Numbers

In the previous pages, you studied patterns with triangles (as in the first picture below).

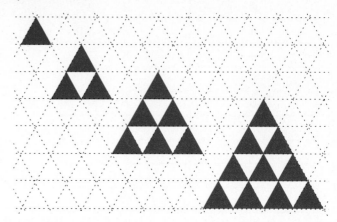

The Greek mathematician Nikomachos, who lived around 100 A.D., studied triangular dot patterns. The numbers, 1, 3, 6, 10,.... are called **triangular numbers**.

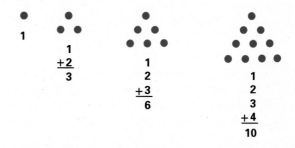

8b Discuss the patterns students find as a class. How does each representation demonstrate the pattern? Be sure students see that they are adding the next number each time, and the connection between the number added and the pattern number.

8. **a.** Describe any connections that you see between the triangular tessellations, the dot patterns, and the triangular numbers.

   b. What regularities do you see in each of the patterns above?

9. The 30th triangular number is 465. Using this fact, what is the 31st triangular number? What is the 29th?

Assessment Pyramid

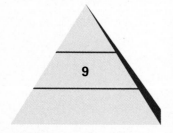

Apply pattern to find next triangular numbers.

Reaching All Learners

Intervention

Some students may need help relating the number added to the pattern number. Review some of the illustrated examples, focusing on this idea. Ask what will be added to go from the 30th to the 31st triangular number. Then ask what was added to go from the 29th to the 30th triangular number.

Accommodation

For problem 8, you may also suggest that students use a number strip and describe the number sequence with an expression.

Solutions and Samples

8. a. Answers will vary. Students should note that the dots represent the number of red tiles in the triangular patterns. Adding a new row of red dots generates the numbers.

b. Sample responses:

The number of red tiles or dots in a bottom row is one more than the number of red tiles or dots in the previous bottom row.

The sequence 1, 3, 6, 10 is generated by adding the number of red tiles or dots in the bottom row to the previous total.

9. The 31st triangular number is 496. The 29th triangular number is 435.

Sample strategy:

To find the 31st and 29th triangular numbers, you can use the 30th triangular number, which is 465. The 31st triangular number has one more row of 31 red dots, so there are 465 + 31, or 496 total red dots. For the 29th triangular number, you can subtract the 30 red dots in the last row of the 30th triangular number, so there are 465 − 30, or 435 total red dots.

Hints and Comments

Overview

Students investigate the connections between triangle tessellations, dot patterns, and triangular numbers.

About the Mathematics

In the previous section, all triangles (red and white) were counted. In this section, only the red tiles are counted. The triangle tessellations (with only red tiles) can be modeled with dot patterns as was done in the first sections of this unit.

Planning

You may want to introduce this section by talking about Nikomachos (see Did You Know? below). Students may work on problems 8 and 9 in small groups.

Comments About the Solutions

8. You may want to make students explicitly aware of the fact that only the red triangles are used.

9. This problem is critical because students use a recursive formula for the sequence of triangular numbers.

Did You Know?

In the first century A.D.., Nikomachos (also known as Nicomachus of Gerasa) wrote *Arithmĕtike eisagooge* (*Introduction to Arithmetic*), which was the first work to treat arithmetic as a separate topic from geometry. Unlike Euclid, Nikomachos gave no abstract proofs of his theorems. He merely stated theorems and illustrated them with numerical examples. Boethius translated Nikomachos's text into Latin. This work was widely used as the standard arithmetic text until the 12th century. It contains the first multiplication table in a Greek text. Nikomachos also wrote *Theologoumena arithmetik⁻es* (*The Theology of Numbers*), which examines mystic properties of numbers.

D Triangles and Triangular Numbers

Notes

10b Share explanations as a class. Look for different strategies. Try to relate explanations to students' ways of visualizing the pattern.

11 You may want to ask students to write a formula for the pattern of rectangular numbers before analyzing the formulas given in the problem.

12b It is helpful if students relate the diagrams to the formulas.

Rectangular Numbers

Nikomachos was interested in finding a direct formula for the triangular numbers.

As part of his investigation, he used a pattern he called the **rectangular numbers**.

| 1 | 2 | 3 | 4 |

The rectangular numbers are 2, 6, 12, 20, and so on.

10. **a.** Find the next three rectangular numbers.

    b. Is 132 a rectangular number? Explain why or why not.

11. Ann wrote the formula $R = n(n + 1)$ for rectangular numbers. Barbara wrote a different formula: $R = n^2 + n$. Use dot patterns to explain both Ann's formula and Barbara's formula.

12. **a.** Make a drawing to demonstrate that each rectangular number is double a triangular number.

    b. Nikomachos found a direct formula for the triangular numbers:

    the nth triangular number = $\frac{1}{2}n(n + 1)$,

    where n starts at 1.

    Explain this formula.

13. In problem 9, you found the 29th, 30th, and 31st triangular numbers. Use Nikomachos's formula to check those values.

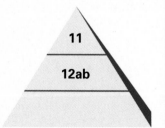
Reaching All Learners

Intervention

For problem 12, if students have trouble seeing this, suggest they divide the rectangular array in half diagonally.

Connection

Connect formulas for rectangular numbers and triangular numbers to the corresponding formulas for the area of rectangles and triangles.

Solutions and Samples

10. a. 30, 42, 56. These are 5 × 6, 6 × 7, and 7 × 8, respectively.

   b. Yes; 11 × 12 = 132, and since 132 is the product of consecutive numbers, it is a rectangular number.

11. For Ann's formula, $R = n(n + 1)$:

Finding the number of dots forming the rectangle is similar to finding its area, which is length $(n + 1)$ times width (n), or $n(n + 1)$.

Ann: n

$n + 1$

For Barbara's formula, $R = n^2 + n$

Barbara: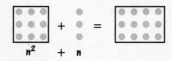

$n^2 \quad + \quad n$

12. a. Sample drawing:

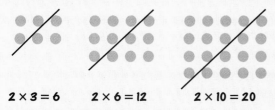

$2 \times 3 = 6 \qquad 2 \times 6 = 12 \qquad 2 \times 10 = 20$

Each rectangular dot pattern can be divided into two halves that are triangles.

   b. A rectangular number is twice a triangular number. The formula for a rectangular number is $n(n + 1)$. The formula for a triangular number is half the formula for a rectangular number, thus $\frac{1}{2}n(n + 1)$.

13. $\frac{1}{2} \times 29 \times 30 = 435$, for $n = 29$

   $\frac{1}{2} \times 30 \times 31 = 465$, for $n = 30$

   $\frac{1}{2} \times 31 \times 32 = 496$, for $n = 31$

Hints and Comments

Overview

Rectangular numbers are introduced. Students create and use formulas for rectangular and triangular numbers.

About the Mathematics

In the formulas for rectangular and triangular numbers, n starts at 1. For the rectangular numbers, n is the length of the vertical side of the rectangular pattern, and for the triangular numbers n is the length of the base of the triangular dot pattern.

A rectangular dot pattern can be cut into two halves along the diagonal so that each half has an equal number of dots. Each half is a triangular dot pattern. Dot patterns can help students visualize expressions and better understand the equivalency of formulas.

Planning

You may want to introduce rectangular numbers, then have a class discussion to see whether students understand what triangular and rectangular numbers are. Students may work on problems 10–12 in small groups and on problem 13 individually.

Comments About the Solutions

10. A rectangular number is the total number of dots arranged to form a rectangle in which the length is one dot longer than the width.

11. and 12.
Students may come up with different explanations. When discussing these problems, you may want to ask students to come up to the board and draw their solutions. This can help the discussion about the equivalency of formulas.

12. This problem is critical because it provides an alternative expression for the sequence of triangular numbers.

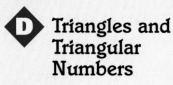

A Wall of Cans

14. How many cans will fit in a triangular display against this wall?

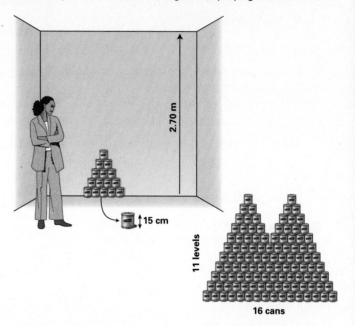

2.70 m

15 cm

11 levels

16 cans

The manager of a store wants to try a new way to stack cans. She thinks a camel shape would be more eye-catching, but she is not sure how many cans would be needed to build that shape.

Use **Student Activity Sheet 3** to help you solve problem 15.

15. a. If the display is to be 16 cans wide with 17 levels, study the drawing and find the number of cans needed for the display.

b. Write the steps in your calculation. Make sure your steps are clear so that you could follow those same steps for a different number of cans in the bottom layer and for a different number of levels.

c. Design a new display. Draw the shape for your own arrangement of cans. Include the important measurements and predict how many cans will be required.

15 If students need help to start the problem, ask them how they might apply the ideas of triangular numbers here. Look for a variety of student strategies.

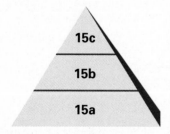

Assessment Pyramid

15c

15b

15a

Use formulas to describe triangular number patterns in realistic situations.

Reaching All Learners

Intervention

If students have trouble with problem 15, ask them to draw triangles on the activity sheet. They can be triangles of cans that are there, or triangles representing missing cans. Ask how many cans are in the base of each triangle. How can the number of cans in the bottom row help us find how many cans are in each triangular stack?

Solutions and Samples

14. 171 cans. Students should first find how many lengths of 15 centimeters go into 2.70 meters (270 cm). There are $270 \div 15 = 18$ cans that fit. A stack 18 cans high is also 18 cans wide at the base. So the total number of cans in the stack will be equal to: *18th triangular number* $= \frac{1}{2} \times 18 \times 19 = 171$.

15. a. and **b.**

111 cans. Strategies will vary.
Sample strategies:

You can think of the shape as a full triangular stack of 16, with a stack of 5 (16 − 11) and a stack of 4 (one less than 5) missing.

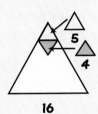

16th triangular number $= \frac{1}{2} \times 16 \times 17 = 136$
5th triangular number $= \frac{1}{2} \times 5 \times 6 = 15$
4th triangular number $= \frac{1}{2} \times 4 \times 5 = 10$
So the answer is $136 - 15 - 10 = 111$.

Another way to solve this problem is as follows: There are two full triangles with 11 cans along the bottom row. These triangles overlap forming a triangle with 6 cans along the bottom row.

To find the total number of cans, there would be two 11th triangular numbers minus one 6th triangular number.

$2(\frac{1}{2} \times 11 \times 12) - (\frac{1}{2} \times 6 \times 7)$
$= 132 - 21$
$= 111$

c. Answers will vary. One possible configuration:

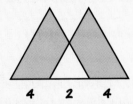

Using the second method from problem 10a above, $2(\frac{1}{2} \times 6 \times 7) - (\frac{1}{2} \times 2 \times 3) = 39$ cans.

Hints and Comments

Materials

Student Activity Sheet 3 (one per student)

Overview

Students use triangular numbers and Nikomachos's formula to calculate how many cans are needed for a store display.

About the Mathematics

To calculate the number of items (cans in this context) in a pattern that can be arranged into triangular patterns, you can calculate the number of items in the smaller (triangular) parts and combine these numbers to find the total number of items needed.

The ability to recognize known shapes and patterns in a complex situation is an important mathematical skill that develops with experience. By using realistic contexts, students will develop the skill of looking for known patterns.

Planning

Students may work on problems 14 and 15 individually.

Comments About the Solutions

14. Students need to use proportional reasoning to find out how many cans with a height of 15 centimeters can be stacked against a wall that is 2.70 meters high.

If students are concerned about the width of the pile fitting along the wall, you can mention that the wall is 5 meters along the base.

D Triangles and Triangular Numbers

Notes

17 Ask students how they can find the number of games without counting all the lines in the graph. Look for a variety of strategies.

18 Share student strategies. Some may look at the pattern of increase, some may find a formula from the graph; some may relate the pattern back to the triangular numbers.

20 Encourage students to relate what is happening in the graph to the real situation. Some students may modify the formula for triangular numbers. Discuss methods students used to develop the formula. Test suggested formulas as a class to verify that they work. You may get several formulas; testing demonstrates whether they are correct and equivalent.

The Ping-Pong Competition

The Jefferson Middle School Student Council wants to organize a ping-pong competition. Everyone who enters the competition will play against everyone else.

The Student Council wants to know how many games will be played. You can use patterns to find the answer for them.

Number of Players	Graph	Number of Games
2		1
3		3
4		6

16. Copy the table into your notebook. Continue the table for five players and for six players.

17. For six players, how many lines are drawn from each vertex?

18. Look at the table to find a pattern. Use your pattern to predict the number of games for seven players and for eight players. Check your answers by extending the table in your notebook.

19. If 50 games are the most that can be played, how many participants can compete?

20. Write a formula that you can use to compute the number of games for any number of players.

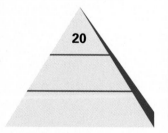

Assessment Pyramid

20

Use formulas to describe patterns in realistic situations.

Reaching All Learners

Act It Out

The ping-pong tournament parallels the classic handshake problem. Have students model the problem using a handshake to represent a game played between two people. Students can model and count the number of games for larger numbers without drawing the graphs.

Intervention

If students are having difficulty with problem 19, suggest they extend the pattern in the table.

Solutions and Samples

16. The table below is extended to include answers to problem 18.

Number of Players	Graph	Number of Games
2		1
3		3
4		6
5		10
6		15
7		21
8		28

17. Five lines

18. Twenty-one matches for seven players; 28 matches for eight players. There are many patterns. Sample responses:

If there are six players, then there are five lines from each vertex (6 × 5), but this counts each game twice, so this number must be divided by two. So, if there are seven players, there are (7 × 6) ÷ 2 = 21 matches, and if there are eight players, there are (8 × 7) ÷ 2 = 28 matches.

Another pattern is that when you add one player, you increase the previous number of games by one less than the new number of players.

7 players: 15 + 6 = 21 games

8 players: 21 + 7 = 28 games

Another pattern is the pattern of triangular numbers started one number later.

7th is $\frac{1}{2} \times 6 \times 7 = 21$

8th is $\frac{1}{2} \times 7 \times 8 = 28$

19. 10 players. The easiest way to show this is to extend the pattern in the table:

9 players: 36 games

10 players: 45 games

11 players: 55 games

20. Let n be the number of players. Direct formula:
number of games $= \frac{1}{2} n(n - 1)$

Hints and Comments

Overview

Students use their knowledge of expressions to describe the pattern needed to solve a problem about the number of matches played in a ping-pong competition.

Planning

This page should help students realize that the formulas and expressions they have been working with up until now also appear in completely different contexts to describe other kinds of patterns. Students may work on these problems individually.

Comments about the Problems

16. It is helpful to arrange the vertices for the graph for 5 and 6 players as the vertices of a pentagon and hexagon.

18. If students do not see a pattern, you may discuss some possible patterns with the class.

20. Here is a possible reasoning process that will lead to the formula:

Each player plays against all other players. So if there are n players, each player plays $n - 1$ matches. Because player A against player B is the same match as player B against player A, the total number of matches is $\frac{1}{2}n(n - 1)$.

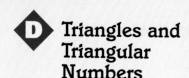

D Triangles and
Triangular
Numbers

Notes

In this section, you found a simple rule: The total number of small triangles that tessellate a larger triangle with n rows equals n^2.

You also studied two types of dot patterns.

Rectangular Pattern   **Triangular Pattern**

The rectangular numbers are 2, 6, 12, 20, and so on.
The nth rectangular number is $n(n + 1)$, where n starts at 1.

The triangular numbers are 1, 3, 6, 10, and so on. When you look at the dot patterns, each rectangular pattern can be divided into two triangular patterns, so the nth triangular number is $\frac{1}{2} n(n + 1)$.

Check Your Work

1 Remind students to use a strategy <u>other</u> than counting each one!

1. **a.** Describe the pattern in the tiles in the tessellation shown in the Summary.

   b. Explain how you can find the total number of red tiles and of white tiles without counting them.

Assessment Pyramid

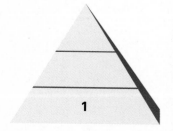

Assesses Section D Goals

Reaching All Learners

Making Connections

For problem 1, you may want to ask students what numbers they are adding in each row or how they could use the formula for triangular numbers to find the answer.

Solutions and Samples

Answers to Check Your Work

1. a. The number of red tiles and the number of white tiles in each row increases according to the pattern in the triangular numbers. The pattern in the red tiles starts with the number 1, and the pattern for the number of white tiles starts with the number 0. You know that because:

- there is a rule that if there are n tiles along the base of a triangular tessellation, then the total number of tiles is equal to n^2. The total number of red and white tiles is 49.

b. You could find the total number of tiles in different ways. For example, look at the pattern for the white tiles:

Row Number from Base	1	2	3	4	5	6	7
Number of White Tiles	6	5	4	3	2	1	0

The total number of white tiles is $6 + 5 + 4 + 3 + 2 + 1 = 21$.

The total number of red tiles is $49 - 21 = 28$.

- You can look at the pattern of the total number of red triangles after each row.

Row Number from Top	1	2	3	4	5	6	7
Total Red Tiles	1	3	6	10	15	21	28

$$+2 \quad +3 \quad +4 \quad +5 \quad +6 \quad +7$$
$$+1 \quad +1 \quad +1 \quad +1 \quad +1$$

- The total number of red tiles is 28, so the number of white tiles would be $49 - 28 = 21$.

Hints and Comments

Overview

Students review the formulas for rectangular and triangular numbers in the Summary. Then they use the Check Your Work problems as self-assessment. The answers to these problems are also provided in the Student Book.

About the Mathematics

Students should realize that what they have learned about manipulating these formulas and expressions can also be accomplished with other formulas and expressions. Discuss how using numerical replacements can help you see if two things are the same but are not really a proof.

Planning

You may want to use the Summary text as the basis for a brief discussion of this section. After students finish this section, you may assign for homework appropriate activities from the Additional Practice, located on Student Book pages 42 and 43.

Notes

2b Hopefully students can expand upon their strategy from part **a**.

3 If students have trouble, have them find a triangle of dots that would help. They can then add (or subtract) extra dots in the last row.

---

2. **a.** Suppose you have a stack of pipes, like the one shown on the right, with 5 pipes on the bottom and 1 pipe on the top. Compute the number of pipes in the stack. Use some method other than counting each one.

   b. Compute the number of pipes in a stack that has 25 pipes on the bottom and 1 pipe on the top. Use some method other than counting each one.

   c. Design and solve your own pipe problem.

3. If you started counting the dots from the top of the triangle, going down by rows, how many dots in total have you counted when you reach the circled dot? Use what you know about triangular numbers to answer this problem.

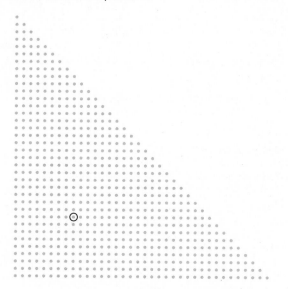

Assessment Pyramid

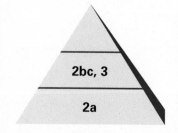

2bc, 3

2a

Assesses Section D Goals

Reaching All Learners

Advanced Learners

You might challenge advanced learners to find the number of pipes in a stack with a top number greater than 1 (a truncated stack). You can also challenge them to write a formula to use for a stack of pipes with any number on the bottom and any (smaller) number on top.

Intervention

If students have difficulty with problem 2 or 3, review the connection between the number of dots in the bottom row, the pattern number, and the formula for triangular numbers. Review the connections between the formula and the dot pattern for smaller values of n, then extend it.

Solutions and Samples

2. a. 15 pipes.

   b. 325 pipes. Sample strategies:

     Using Nikomachos's formula to find the 25th triangular number:

$$= \frac{1}{2} \times 25 \times (25 + 1)$$
$$= \frac{1}{2} \times 25 \times 26$$
$$= 325$$

     By adding the first and last rows, and then the second and next-to-last rows, and so on, you get 12 groups of 26 plus the 13 in the middle: $12 \times 26 + 13 = 325$.

   c. Problems will vary. Sample problem:

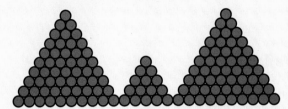

     The left and right triangles are identical and have 10 pipes in the base; the middle triangle has a base of five pipes.

     Using Nikomachos's formula:

$$2 \times \frac{1}{2}(10 \times 11) + \frac{1}{2}(5 \times 6)$$
$$= 110 + 15$$
$$= 125.$$

3. 387. Sample strategy:

   You may think about this problem in different ways. One way is to count the number of dots in the row above the circled dot, which is 27. The 27th triangular number is $\frac{1}{2}(27 \times 28) = 378$. Adding on the nine dots in the row with the circled dot, you get $378 + 9 = 387$.

Hints and Comments

Overview

Students use the Check Your Work problems as self-assessment. The answers to these problems are also provided in the Student Book.

Planning

After students finish this section, you may assign as homework appropriate activities from the Additional Practice, located on Student Book pages 42 and 43.

Notes

4 Students can continue
their patterns from the
ping-pong tournament or
apply the formula they
developed.

 Triangles and Triangular Numbers

In the MiC Tennis Tournament, everyone who enters the competition
will play against everyone else. Suppose 12 players from Rydell
Middle School will play.

4. How many games do the 12 players play in total?

Before the tournament starts, each participant shakes hands with all
competitors.

5. How many handshakes are given in total?

 For Further Reflection

Find a situation that has the same mathematical content as the
ping-pong tournament and the handshake problem.

Assessment Pyramid

Assesses Section D Goals

Reaching All Learners

Parent Involvement

Have parents review the section with their child to relate the Check Your
Work problems to the problems in this section.

Solutions and Samples

4. If you need help with this problem, look at the ping-pong competition.

The number of games is $\frac{1}{2} \times 12 \times 11 = 66$.

5. The number of handshakes is the same as the number of games, 66.

For Further Reflection
Any game where two participants play against one another may serve as an example. But you can also think of a party game where every participant changes the coin they have in their hands with every other participant.

Hints and Comments

Overview
Students use the Check Your Work problems as self-assessment. The answers to these problems are also provided in the Student Book.

Additional Practice

Section Ⓐ Patterns

1. Write the first five numbers in each of the sequences described by the following expressions. For each expression, n starts at zero.

   a. $2n + 3$

   b. $15n - 10$

   c. $\frac{1}{2}n + \frac{1}{2}$

2. Make your own expression and write the first five numbers of the sequence represented by your expression. Make sure n starts at zero.

3. a. Write a NEXT-CURRENT formula for the dot pattern shown below.

   b. Describe the dot pattern with a direct formula $D = \ldots\ldots$

Dot Pattern:	●●● ●●● ●●●	● ●●● ●●● ●●●	●●● ●●● ●●● ●●●
Pattern Number:	2	3	4

4. a. Make a number strip for the formula

   NEXT number = CURRENT number + 4, with starting number 17

   b. Write an expression that represents the sequence.

Section A. Patterns

1. a. 3, 5, 7, 9, 11

  b. −10, 5, 20, 35, 50

  c. $\frac{1}{2}$, 1, $1\frac{1}{2}$, 2, $2\frac{1}{2}$

2. Answers will vary depending on the expression students chose.

3. a. START number = 7

  NEXT number of dots = CURRENT number of dots + 3

  b. Sample student answer: $D = 3 \times n + 1$, n starts at 2.

4. a.

  b. $17 + 4n$ or $4n + 17$; n starts at 0

Additional Practice

Section ◆B◆ Sequences

Joey and Alice collect old magazines for their school. Joey has currently collected 24 magazines. Each week he gets three more old magazines.

1. Make a number strip that begins with 24 and gives the number of magazines Joey has at the end of each week.

2. How many magazines will Joey have after *n* weeks?

Alice currently has 39 magazines. Each week she collects two magazines.

3. How many magazines will Alice have after *n* weeks?

4. How many magazines will Joey and Alice collect together after *n* weeks?

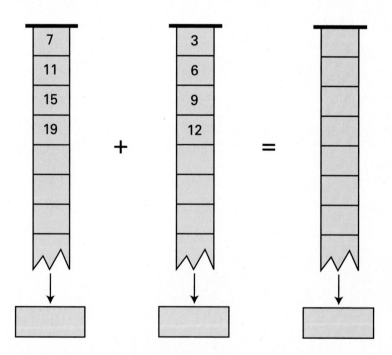

5. Copy and complete the missing parts of the three number strips shown above. Let *n* start at zero for all three number strips.

Section B. Sequences

1.

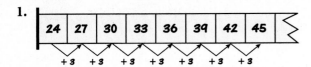

2. $24 + 3n$

3. $39 + 2n$

4. $63 + 5n$

5.

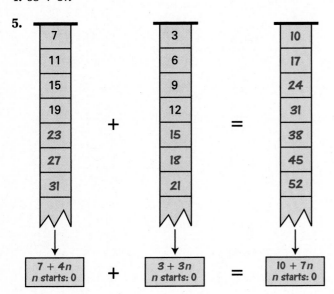

6. Copy and complete the missing parts of the number strip subtraction shown below. Let *n* start at zero for all three number strips.

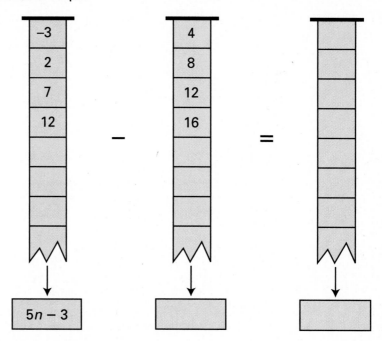

−3	4	
2	8	
7	12	
12	16	

−   =

$5n - 3$

Section ◆C Square Numbers

Here is a sequence of four tile patterns. *P* stands for the pattern number.

  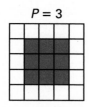 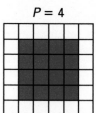

$P = 1$ $P = 2$ $P = 3$ $P = 4$

1. Write a direct formula to calculate the number of green tiles needed for each pattern number (*P*). Note that *P* starts at one in this problem!

2. Explain using the tile patterns above that the formula for the number of white tiles for pattern number *P* is

   number of white tiles = 4 × (*P* + 1)

Section B. Sequences (continued)

6.
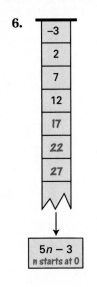
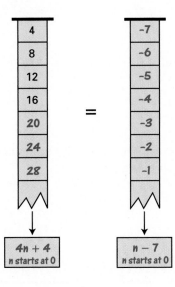

Section C. Square Numbers

1. *number of green tiles = P × P* or *number of green tiles = P²*

2. Explanations will vary. Students may plug in the numbers from the given patterns:

   For $P = 1$, the result is $4 \times (1+1) = 8$

   For $P = 2$, the result is $4 \times (2+1) = 12$

   For $P = 3$, the result is $4 \times (3+1) = 16$

   For $P = 4$, the result is $4 \times (4+1) = 20$

   The number of white tiles can be broken down into four parts, to make a total of

   $4 \times (P + 1)$ tiles.

Additional Practice

3. What is the formula for the total number of tiles?

4. Explain how the formulas you found in problems 1, 2, and 3 are related.

5. Use an area diagram to show that the expressions $n^2 + 4n + 4$ and $(n + 2)^2$ are equivalent.

Section Ⓓ Triangles and Triangular Numbers

A tetrahedron is a regular three-dimensional shape with four equal faces. The faces each have the shape of an equilateral triangle. A picture of a tetrahedron is shown.

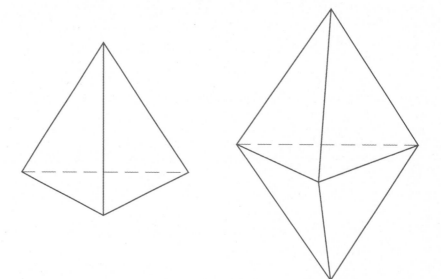

Anton has started to cover each face with blue and white triangular tiles.

He can fit 11 blue tiles along each edge.

1. How many tiles (blue and white) does Anton need to completely cover the tetrahedron?

Section C. Square Numbers (continued)

3. The total number of tiles is $(P + 2) \times (P + 2)$, or $(P + 2)^2$; this is the combination of the two previous formulas, $P^2 + 4 \times (P + 1)$.

Sample strategy:

The total number of tiles is $(P + 2) \times (P + 2)$ because the length of the square is $P + 2$.

4. The formula from problem 3 = the formula for problem 1 + the formula for problem 2

Or $(P + 2)^2 = P^2 + 4 \times (P + 1)$

5. Sample student answer:

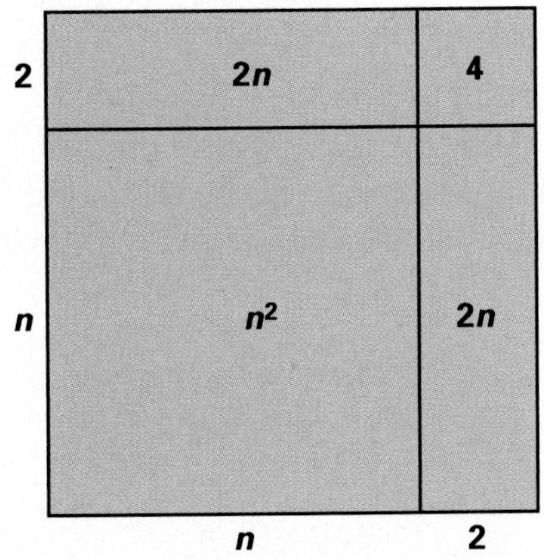

[Diagram of a square divided into four regions. Left side labeled 2 (top) and n (bottom); bottom labeled n (left) and 2 (right). Top-left region: 2n; top-right region: 4; bottom-left region: n^2; bottom-right region: 2n.]

$(n + 2)^2 = n^2 + 2n + 2n + 4 = n^2 + 4n + 4$

Section D. Triangles and Triangular Numbers

1. 484 tiles. Students should figure that, for one face, Anton needs $11^2 = 121$ triangular tiles. The tetrahedron has four equal faces; therefore, the total number of tiles is $4 \times 121 = 484$.

You can paste two tetrahedra together as shown in the figure.

2. How many tiles are needed to completely cover this new shape?

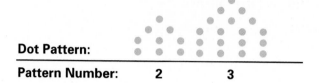

Dot Pattern:

Pattern Number: **2**   **3**

3. Study the dot pattern above and draw the pattern for $n = 4$.

You can split each pattern in a triangle and a rectangle so that the base of the triangle has as many dots as the right side of the rectangle. The following is a sketch of how the shape can be split into a triangle and a rectangle.

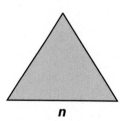

n

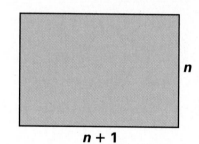

n

n + 1

4. a. Draw the triangle for the pattern $n = 5$.

   b. Draw the rectangle for the pattern $n = 5$.

   c. How many dots are needed for the pattern $n = 5$?

5. Write an expression for the number of dots for pattern *n*. Use the sketch above.

Section D. Triangles and Triangular Numbers (continued)

2. $6 \times 121 = 726$ tiles. The new shape has a total number of six sides. (Two separate tetrahedra have eight sides, but when they are joined, two faces "disappear.")

3.

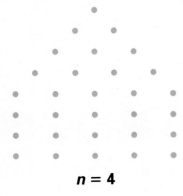

n = 4

4. a. and **b.**

c. 45 dots. Sample explanation: for the rectangle, the area is $6 \times 5 = 30$; for the triangle, the area is $\frac{1}{2} \times 5 \times 6 = 15$; so combined is: 45 dots

5. $1\frac{1}{2}n(n+1)$. Students may reason as follows:

For the rectangle: $n \times (n + 1)$

For the triangle: $\frac{1}{2}n(n + 1)$, so combined:

$n(n + 1) + \frac{1}{2}n(n + 1) = 1\frac{1}{2}n(n + 1)$

Assessment Overview

Assessment Overview

Unit assessments in *Mathematics in Context* include two quizzes and Unit Test. Quiz 1 is to be used anytime after students have completed Section B. Quiz 2 can be used after students have completed Section C. The Unit Test addresses most of the major goals of the unit. You can evaluate student responses to these assessments to determine what each student knows about the content goals addressed in this unit.

Pacing

Each quiz is designed to take approximately 25 minutes to complete. The Unit Test is designed to be completed during a 45-minute class period. For more information on how to use these assessments, see the Planning Assessment section on the next page.

Goals	Assessment Opportunities		Problem Levels
• Use and create dot patterns, number strips, or charts to visualize number sequences.	Quiz 1 Test	Problems 1, 3a Problems 2b, 3ab, 4ab	
• Create and use recursive formulas to describe number sequences	Quiz 1	Problem 2b	
• Create and use expressions and direct formulas to describe number sequences.	Quiz 1 Test	Problems 1, 2a, 3a Problems 2cd, 3ab	I
• Understand arithmetic sequences.	Quiz 1 Quiz 2 Test	Problems 1, 2a, 3a Problems 3a, 4a Problem 2ab	
• Understand the sequence of square numbers.	Quiz 2 Test	Problems 1, 2 Problems 1abc	
• Combine (add or subtract) number sequences and the corresponding expressions.	Quiz 1	Problem 1	II
• Justify equivalent expressions.	Quiz 1 Test	Problems 3bc Problems 2d, 3b	
• Use triangular numbers as examples of describing sequences.	Test	Problems 4cde	
• Use visual models to represent equivalent expressions and formulas.	Quiz 2 Test	Problem 3b Problems 4cd	
• Generalize a concrete number sequence as an expression.	Quiz 2	Problems 4de	III
• Use formulas and expressions to describe patterns and sequences in realistic situations.	Test	Problem 4d	

44 Patterns and Figures　　　　　　　　　　　　　　　　**Assessment Overview**

About the Mathematics

These assessment activities assess the majority of the goals for *Patterns and Figures*. Refer to the Goals and Assessment Opportunities section on the previous page for information regarding the goals that are assessed in each problem. Some of the problems that involve multiple skills and processes address more than one unit goal. To assess students' ability to engage in non-routine problem solving (a Level III goal in the Assessment Pyramid), some problems assess students' ability to use their skills and conceptual knowledge in new situations. For example, in the T-pattern problem on the Unit Test (Problem 4), students must use visual models to explain the relationship between equivalent formulas.

Planning Assessment

These assessments are designed for individual assessment, however some problems can be done in pairs or small groups. It is important that students work individually if you want to evaluate each student's understanding and abilities.

Make sure you allow enough time for students to complete the problems. If students need more than one class session to complete the problems, it is suggested that they finish during the next mathematics class or you may assign select problems as a take-home activity. Students should be free to solve the problems their own way. Calculators may be used on the quizzes or unit test if students choose to use them.

If individual students have difficulties with any particular problems, you may give the student the option of making a second attempt after providing him/her a hint. You may also decide to use one of the optional problems or Extension activities not previously done in class as additional assessments for students who need additional help.

Scoring

Solution and scoring guides are included for each quiz and the unit test. The method of scoring depends on the types of questions on each assessment. A holistic scoring approach could also be used to evaluate an entire quiz.

Several problems require students to explain their reasoning or justify their answers. For these questions, the reasoning used by students in solving the problems as well as the correctness of the answers should be considered in your scoring and grading scheme.

Student progress toward goals of the unit should be considered when reviewing student work. Descriptive statements and specific feedback are often more informative to students than a total score or grade. You might choose to record descriptive statements of select aspects of student work as evidence of student progress toward specific goals of the unit that you have identified as essential.

Patterns and Figures Quiz 1

Use additional paper as needed.

1. Write an expression for each number sequence *A*, *B*, and *C*.
(Assume *n* starts at zero.)

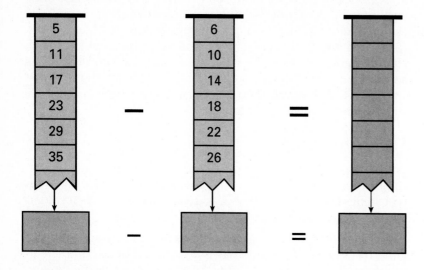

2. a. Make a number strip which results in the expression 6*n* + 1,
where *n* starts at 0.

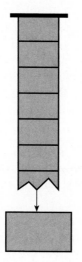

b. Write a NEXT-CURRENT formula for the sequence.

Mathematics in Context

3. You can make a sequence of T-patterns using dots. The first three are shown below:

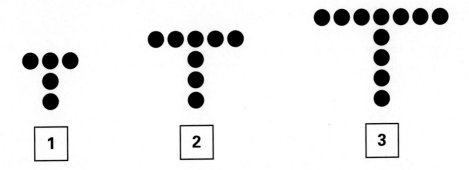

a. Copy and complete this table for the T-patterns.

Number of Dots	5	___	___	___	___	___
Pattern Number	1	2	3	4	5	6

b. Julia and John each wrote a direct formula to describe the number of dots (*n*) in the T-pattern.

Julia wrote the formula $T = 5 + 3(n - 1)$.

John wrote the formula $T = 2 + 3n$.

Show that both formulas are correct.

c. Is it possible to make a T-pattern with 1532 dots? Explain why or why not.

Patterns and Figures Quiz 2

Use additional paper as needed.

1. Peter wants to tile a square patio in his garden. He bought 350 square tiles.

What are the dimensions of the largest square patio that Peter can make? Peter may only use whole tiles.

2. Show that $\left(3\frac{1}{2}\right)^2 = 12\frac{1}{4}$

You may use an area diagram or any other strategy, but not a calculator.

Mathematics in Context

3. The expression n^2 represents the sequence of the square numbers:

0, 1, 4, 16, . . .

If you start the n^2 sequence 4 steps later, you get the $(n + 4)^2$ sequence.

a. Write the first six terms of this sequence.

b. Show that $(n + 4)^2$ is the same as the expression $n^2 + 8n + 16$.

You may use an area diagram.

4. Below is a number strip with an arithmetic sequence.

5						14				20

a. Find the missing numbers in the sequence. Explain how you found your answer.

b. Write an expression to represent the sequence. (Assume n starts at zero.)

Use additional paper as needed.

Growing squares

The drawing shows a sequence of growing squares.

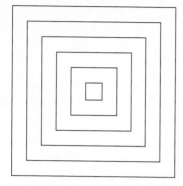

The drawing is not made to scale. The smallest square is
1 centimeter (cm) × 1 centimeter (cm). The second square
from the center is 3 cm × 3 cm, and thus the pattern continues
to the outside.

1. Mary made a number strip showing the first four terms of the
sequence of the areas of the squares.

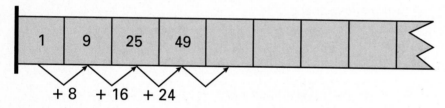

a. Write the next two numbers of the sequence. Explain how
you found these numbers.

b. The numbers of the strip continue with the same pattern.
What will be the 10th number on the strip? Explain your
strategy.

c. Mary says that one of the squares in the sequence has an
area of 900 square centimeters (cm²). Is she right? Explain
why or why not.

Mathematics in Context

2. Peter looks at the perimeter of the squares instead of the areas.

   a. What is the perimeter of the second square? Explain your answer.

   b. Make a number strip showing the sequence of the perimeters of the first five squares.

   c. Write an expression for the strip, n starts at 0. Explain your strategy.

   d. How would the expression change if n starts at 1?

Odd and Even

3. Strip A represents the sequence of the even numbers and Strip B the sequence of the odd numbers.

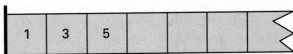

Strip A | 0 | 2 | 4 | | | | |

Strip B | 1 | 3 | 5 | | | | |

   a. What expression describes strip A? And B? (Assume n starts at zero.)

   b. Are the following statements true or false? To explain your reasoning, use the expressions you found for sequences A and B. Or you may use dot-patterns, number strips, or other diagrams.

   _____ The sum of two numbers is even if both numbers are even.

   _____ The sum of two or three or four odd numbers is always an even number.

   _____ The expression $4n^2 + 4n + 1$ describes the sequence of all the squares.

Use additional paper as needed.

Triangular performances

4. Dancers often form triangular figures.

a. If one more row of dancers is added, what is the total number of dancers?

   And if one more row is added again?

   The dancers in any triangle figure form a sequence of triangular numbers.

1	3	6	10	15				

b. Add three more numbers to the strip. Explain how you found these numbers.

In the unit, you have seen this formula for triangular numbers:

the nth triangular number $= \frac{1}{2} n(n + 1)$, where n starts at 1

c. Use this formula to find the total number of dancers if you could have 50 rows of dancers in the triangle.

d. Find the answer for $1 + 2 + 3 + \cdots + 50$.

e. What is the connection with the previous question?

Possible student answer	Suggested number of score points	Problem level
1. Sample student work: 5 11 17 23 29 35 − 6 10 14 18 22 26 = −1 1 3 5 7 9 5 + 6n (n starts at 0) − 6 + 4n (n starts at 0) = −1 + 2n (n starts at 0)	3 (Award 1 score point for each correct expression.)	I/II
2. a. Students should create a number strip with the following numbers: 1, 7, 13, 19, 25, 31, . . .	2	I
b. START NUMBER = 1 NEXT *number* = CURRENT *number* + 6	2	I

3. <table><tr><td>Number of Dots (*T*)</td><td>5</td><td>8</td><td>11</td><td>14</td><td>17</td><td>20</td></tr><tr><td>Pattern Number (*n*)</td><td>1</td><td>2</td><td>3</td><td>4</td><td>5</td><td>6</td></tr></table>	2 (Award 2 score points for all correct values in the table.)	I
b. Answers may vary. Sample student answer: Julia's formula can be written without parentheses $T = 5 + 3(n - 1) = 5 + 3n - 3 = 2 + 3n$ Note: If students try several table entries to show both formulas that give the same result, award 1 score point. Students should be aware that a few examples do not constitute a proof. Some students may also find the formula directly from the pattern. Award 2 score points for correct answer and explanation.	2	II
c. Yes. Sample student work: The total number of dots minus 2 must be divisible by 3. $1532 - 2 = 1530$ and $1530 \div 3 = 510$ OR The total number of dots minus 5 must be divisible by 3. Students may also use a formula found in question 3b: $1532 = 2 + 3n$	2	II
Total score points	13	

Patterns and Figures Unit Test
Solution and Scoring Guide

Possible student answer	Suggested number of score points	Problem level
1. a. 81 and 121. Student explanations should refer to the pattern of adding the next multiple of 8: $+8, +16, +24, +32, +40$, and so on.	1	I
b. The 10th number on the strip is 361. Students may extend the strip to the 10th entry using the first and second differences.	2	I

1	9	25	49	81	121	169	225

$+8 \quad +16 \quad +24 \quad +32 \quad +40 \quad +48$

$+8 \quad +8 \quad +8 \quad +8 \quad +8$

Or they may use a pattern they see in the numbers.

Square Number	Area	
1	$1 \times 1 = 1$	
2	$3 \times 3 = 9$	$(4 - 1) \times (4 - 1) = 9$
3	$5 \times 5 = 25$	$(6 - 1) \times (6 - 1) = 25$
4	$7 \times 7 = 49$	$(8 - 1) \times (8 - 1) = 49$
5	$9 \times 9 = 81$	$(10 - 1) \times (10 - 1) = 81$
. . .	. . .	. . .
10	361	$(20 - 1) \times (20 - 1) = 361$

Possible student answer	Suggested number of score points	Problem level
c. No. Explanations will vary: $900 = 30^2$ and 30 is an even number. OR 900 is an even number and in the sequence there are only odd numbers.	2	I
2. a. The perimeter is 12 cm. Sample student work: $3 + 3 + 3 + 3 = 12$ OR $3 \times 4 = 12$	1	I
b.	1	I

4	12	20	28	36	

$+8 \quad +8 \quad +8 \quad +8$

Possible student answer	Suggested number of score points	Problem level
c. Sample student answer: $4 + 8n$. The first square has perimeter 4, and each perimeter of square increases by 8. Award full score if student finds an equivalent expression to $4 + 8n$ with adequate explanation.	2	I

Possible student answer	Suggested number of score points	Problem level
d. The expression depends on the strategy used for the solution to problem 2c. Sample student answer: $4 + 8(n - 1)$ OR $4 \times (2n - 1)$ Or $8n - 4$	1	I/II
3. a. Sample student work: Expression of strip A: $2n$ Expression of strip B: $2n + 1$	2	I
b. The first statement is correct. Sample student answer: An even number is always a multiple of two; if you add two multiples of two, you still have a multiple of two. $2n + 2m = 2(m + n)$ The second statement is not correct. Sample student answer: 3, 5, and 7 are odd numbers, and their sum is also an odd number. The third statement is not correct. Sample student answer: If you substitute n in the expression by number 1, 2, 3, you get only the odd square numbers 9, 25, 49.	6 (Award 2 points for each correct answer with an explanation.)	I/II
4 a. $21(15 + 6)$ and $28(21 + 7)$	1	I
b. 21, 28, and 36. Explanations may vary. Sample explanation: 	2	I
c. *Total number of dancers* $= \frac{1}{2} \times 50 \times 51 = 1{,}275$	1	II/III
d. $1 + 2 + 3 + \cdots + 50 = 1{,}275.$	2	II/III
e. Explanations may vary. Sample explanation: the connection with the previous question is: $1 + 2 + 3 + \ldots + 50$ is exactly the total number of dancers in a triangular form with 50 rows.	2	II/III
Total score points	26	

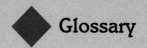 Glossary

Glossary

The glossary defines all vocabulary words indicated in this unit. It includes the mathematical terms that may be new to students, as well as words having to do with the contexts introduced in the unit. (Note: The Student Book has no Glossary. Instead, students are encouraged to construct their own definitions, based on their personal experiences with the unit activities.)

The definitions below are specific for the use of the terms in this unit. The page numbers given are from the Student Book.

arithmetic sequence (p. 10) a list of numbers in which each number in the sequence is related to the next number in the sequence by a constant increase or decrease

direct formula (p. 3) a formula that can be used to determine any value in a sequence given its position in the sequence

Euler's formula (p. 17) a formula that relates the numbers of vertices, faces, and edges in polyhedra ($V - E + F = 2$)

icosahedron (p. 17) a regular 20-face polyhedron built from equilateral triangles

NEXT-CURRENT formula (p. 3) a formula describing the next value in a sequence based on the current value

pattern number (p. 2) a number describing the position of a value in a sequence

polyhedra (p. 18) three-dimensional solid which consists of a collection of polygons, usually joined at their edges.

rectangular number (p. 33) the area of a rectangle with length $n + 1$ and side n; the sequence of rectangular numbers is 2, 6, 12, 20, . . .

recursive formula (p. 3) see NEXT-CURRENT formula

sequence (p. 2) numbers usually arranged according to some pattern

square number (p. 21) the result of the multiplication of a number by itself; the sequence of (perfect) square numbers is 1, 4, 9, 16, 25, . . .

tessellation (p. 30) the complete covering of a plane or shape or other two-dimensional area with copies of a single figure

triangular number (p. 32) a number that is one-half of a rectangular number; the sequence of triangular numbers is 1, 3, 6, 10…

vertex (p. 16) the point of intersection of edges of polyhedron or the sides of a polygon

Blackline Masters

Dear Family,

Your child will soon begin the *Mathematics in Context* unit *Patterns and Figures*. Below is a letter to your child that opens the unit, describing the unit and its goals.

In this unit, students think about number patterns and geometric shapes. The study of patterns is one of the most important mathematical pursuits. Your child will study different ways to describe patterns using words, numbers, pictures, and formulas.

Some interesting number patterns were investigated by early mathematicians. You can assist your child by helping him or her investigate the lives and contributions of mathematicians such as Sophie Germain, Johann and Jakob Bernoulli, Emmy Noether, and Leonard Euler. Perhaps one of their discoveries can be shared with others in the class. You might challenge your child to discover his or her own interesting number patterns. Encourage your child t o share other discoveries with you. For example, near the end of the unit ask him or her about triangular and rectangular numbers.

We hope both you and your child enjoy the unit and find it a worthwhile experience.

Sincerely,

The Mathematics in Context Development Team

Dear Student,

Welcome to the unit *Patterns and Figures*. In this unit, you will identify patterns in numbers and shapes and describe those patterns using words, diagrams, and formulas.

You have already seen many patterns in mathematics. For patterns with certain characteristics, you will learn rules and formulas to help you describe them. Some of the patterns are described by using geometric figures, and others are described by a mathematical relationship.

Here are two patterns. One is a pattern of dots, and the other is a pattern of geometric shapes.

Can you describe the dot pattern? Where do you think the pattern of shapes ends?

As you investigate the *Patterns and Figures* unit, remember that patterns exist in many places—almost anywhere you look! The skills you develop in looking for and describing patterns will always help you, both inside and outside your math classroom.

Sincerely,

The Mathematics in Context Development Team

Name _____

Student Activity Sheet 1
Use with *Patterns and Figures*, page 3.

Direct and Recursive Formulas for Sequences on the Calculator

The graphing calculator uses a different way to write these formulas:

Recursive: u(*n*) = u(*n* − 1) + 2
- This means that the next u value is equal to the previous u value plus 2
- Here u(*n*) replaces the NEXT-RED and u(*n* − 1) replaces the CURRENT-RED

Direct: v(*n*) = 2*n*
- This means that the sequence v equals two times *n*
- Here the v(*n*) replaces the R

I. Set the calculator to the initial sequence settings

Press [MODE] (QUIT) and arrow down and over to **Seq** to select the sequence setting. Highlight **Seq** by pressing [ENTER]. The screen on the right shows the sequence mode highlighted in the fourth row.

Next, set the start value (TblStart) and the step size (∆Tbl) for the sequence. Press [2nd] [WINDOW] (TBLSET) and set the numbers as shown on the right.

II. Enter the two formulas from above and look at the table of values

To access the sequence formula screen press [Y=] (STAT PLOT). For the recursive formula fill in the following values:

nMin = [0] (CATALOG ⌐)

u(*n*) = [2nd] [7] (u) [(] (o) [{] (K) [X,T,Θ,n] (LINK) [−] (]) [1] (W) [)] (L1) (Y) [+] (}) (L) [2] (MEM) (") (L2) (Z)

u(*n*Min) = [0] (CATALOG ⌐)

For the direct formula fill in values:

v(*n*) = [2] (L2) (Z) [X,T,Θ,n] (LINK)

v(*n*Min) = [0] (CATALOG ⌐)

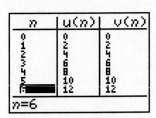

III. Examine the table of values

Now look at the table of values for the two sequences. Press [2nd] [GRAPH] (TABLE). Your table should look like the one on the right.

Notice the *n* values start at 0 (you set this up in part I) and *n* increases by 1 each step.

Student Activity Sheet 2
Use with *Patterns and Figures*, page 30.

Name _____

6. a. Starting with Figure I, reflect every white triangle over the base of the triangle (Figure II). Color each reflected triangle red (Figure III).

b. Explain why the total number of tiles in Figure I is equal to the number of red tiles in the finished version of Figure III.

c. The rule states that the total number of tiles in Figure I is equal to 4^2. Explain this using the finished version of Figure III.

d. Verify the rule for a triangle with five rows ($n = 5$).

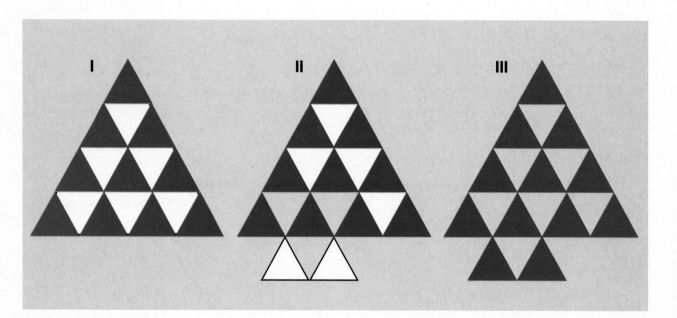

Name _____

Student Activity Sheet 3
Use with *Patterns and Figures*, page 34.

15. a. If the display is to be 16 cans wide with 17 levels, study the drawing and find the number of cans needed for the display.

   b. Write the steps in your calculation. Explain what you would have to change so you could follow those same steps for a different number of cans in the bottom layer and for a different number of levels.

   c. Design a new display. Draw the shape for your own arrangement of cans. Include the important measurements and predict how many cans will be required.

11 levels

16 cans